STEPHEN SELBY

AN INSIGHT INTO DEPRESSION

- FINDING HAPPINESS AND INSTILLING HOPE

Publisher: Independent Publishing Network.
Publication date: March 2019
First Edition
ISBN: 978-1-78926-979-6
Author: Stephen Selby
Email: depressionbook@stephenselby.com
Please direct all enquiries to the author.

DISCLAIMER
The contents of this book are intended for personal study, discussion and to raise awareness around various factors that may impact depression. The publisher and author(s) shall not be held liable for any actions, thoughts, or changes (including changes to medication) that readers take as a direct result of reading this book. Neither the publisher nor the individual author(s) shall be liable for any physical, psychological, emotional, financial, or commercial damages, including, but not limited to, special, incidental, consequential or other damages. Our views and rights are the same: You are responsible for your own choices, actions, and results.

The information provided in this book is designed to provide helpful information on the subjects discussed. This book is not

TABLE OF CONTENTS

INTRODUCTION

Thank you for taking the time to read this book. I am aware that reading a book during a depressive episode can be a little overwhelming. Please be kind to yourself. You may find it difficult to concentrate for long periods – so take it slowly. In order to get the most out of this book, I recommend the following approaches:-

1. Don't expect this book to solve all your issues – seek out other sources of help.

2. Don't try to read more than a page or two at a time.

3. You may forget a lot – so re-read sections.

4. Use a pen or pencil to highlight anything you find useful.

5. Stop and think about points that are raised.

6. For a quick read – scan through the book and look at the bold printed phrases and summaries.

This book is not a comprehensive guide to everything about depression. We will touch on a variety of subjects that you may want to research in more depth. My hope is that it will get you thinking and talking about the issues that arise.

I also hope you can have an open mind. I am a work in progress. In years to come some of my viewpoints on depression may change. So if there are things you disagree with, then that is fine. In fact, if you disagree, it shows that you have thought about what I have said.

One more thing. I would love to hear from people who have benefited from this book. So please feel free to write to me using the contact details below.

I hope you find this book helpful.

Stephen

email: depressionbook@stephenselby.com

COVER PAINTING

The cover painting "Courage of a Warrior, Light of the Divine" is by a talented local artist: Jayne Tricker. The painting was based on an area near Cleeve Hill, Cheltenham in the Cotswolds, UK. Each year an area of bushes and trees are cut down and burnt in a fire. For me, dead wood is a great symbol of those things that cause depression. The fire in the valley shows us there is hope amongst the dark times of life.

You can find more wonderful paintings at her website:

https://www.jaynetrickerart.co.uk/

WHAT IS DEPRESSION?

Defining depression

"The state of feeling very unhappy and without hope for the future"
Cambridge Dictionary

"A mental illness that causes feelings of sadness and loss of hope, changes in sleeping and eating habits, loss of interest in your usual activities, and pains that have no [seemingly] physical explanation"
Cambridge Dictionary

"A mental condition characterized by feelings of severe despondency and dejection, typically also with feelings of inadequacy and guilt, often accompanied by lack of energy and disturbance of appetite and sleep"
Oxford Dictionary

"A mental disorder characterized by extreme gloom, feelings of inadequacy, and inability to concentrate"
Collins Dictionary

The library is dark, blackness surrounds me.
I no longer want to go on,
I click,
I fumble for a switch,
I click;
But there is no light.

I search.
There is supposed to be a white book here amongst
the dusty shelves.
The books are heavy and old.
My hands drag them from the shelves and they
crash to the floor,
But all I can smell is dark, black, leather.

I sift through them one by one lifting each back to
its place,
It's so much effort that my bones groan.
I'm walled in,
I cry out in the dark but no one hears me,
I hear my own voice rattle inside my head:
I am, I should have, I can't, I must.

Everyone says there is a room next door,
A white room, with white books and light
streaming through the window.
How do I get there? My muscles feel torn.
The ceiling looms over me like black hands, ready
to strangle me.
Alone, the past haunts me,
The future is empty.
My mind whirs:
I will never; I can't.

Stephen Selby

4

Depression has become an increasingly common problem in today's society. Prescriptions for antidepressants have sky-rocketed and mental health services are under strain. In this book, I hope to share my insights about depression.

It is very difficult to describe how you feel when you're depressed. I have tried to capture it above in some words; nonetheless, I feel that depression can be better described by music, by a dissonant cluster or angst line on the violins; but this is a book where we are limited to words. Having suffered with depression I hope the content of this book will resonate with your own experiences. During my worst episodes, I was treated like a human guinea-pig with various medications (Citalopram, Sertraline, Venlefaxine). I was signed off work sick, constantly ruminated about suicide, tried counselling in various forms, and ended up having to be looked after by my parents because I couldn't cope.

Whilst I cannot claim to be 100% depression free I no longer suffer with the severe long-term depression I used to have. Periods tend to be shorter, I no longer take medication and have hope for the future. What do I put it down to? There are a lot of factors which are outlined in this book. Ultimately, I would put it down to understanding the underlying causes and being more self-aware. Does that mean I am depression free? I am free in as much as I choose to maintain it. Just like someone who is physically fit has to maintain their fitness, you have to maintain your mental health. A lot of this has to do with your memory. If I started to forget everything I've learnt about hope, I could slip back into depression. As you will find out, developing a good memory is a key part of overcoming depression and instilling hope. I am also less likely to slip back into depression as my circumstances are drastically different from what they were when I was depressed. Occasionally we come across a new problem. If we haven't got the tools to deal with it, or find an answer, it can propel us toward depression. If this is the case, there are two possible answers as follows:

1. Try to find the specific solution
2. Build character to cope with the problem.

What is depression?
We all have ups and downs in life. We all have peaks and troughs. However, these vary in length and intensity. Low periods can often come immediately after having high levels of adrenaline, such as going to a party, but we normally recover quickly. Even if something bad happens, we generally "bounce back" quickly to our normal self. Here is a graph to represent a fairly normal person:

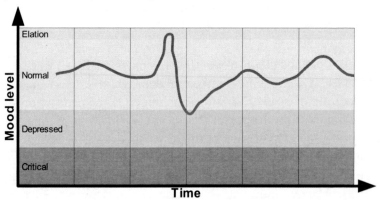

In the graph above we see someone who has a moment of happiness followed by a dip into depression. However, this person recovers fairly quickly.

When the troughs are extremely low, or people do not recover, these can be seen as periods of depression. Some people continue for months, and others years. In order to be clinically depressed the diagnosis requires a low-mood for at least two weeks. The following person has slipped into depression:

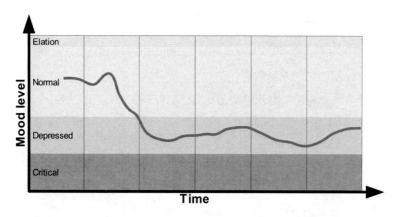

In the graph above we can see that the person's mood has not recovered to normal.

Someone who would be described as normal may be happy 95% of the time, and 5% of the time have low mood. Someone who suffers with depression may be low 90% of the time and 10% of the time be happy. Depression is more about the frequency and intensity of these low moods.

How is depression diagnosed?
Depression is often diagnosed by a doctor, but this is not based on any physical test. Doctors normally use questionnaires over several weeks to determine whether low mood is a temporary (less than a two-week period) or more permanent form of depression. The diagnosis is based on a variety of symptoms, including the following:

7

Symptoms

- Lack of attention span – attention for tasks is limited
- Disturbed sleep
- A feeling that everything is pointless
- Lack of hope
- Lack of motivation
- Lack of passion
- Fatigue
- Suicidal thoughts
- Negative Rumination
- Obsession
- Anxiety
- Headaches
- Over or under-eating
- Paranoia
- Feelings that friends are talking behind your back
- Creative block
- Guilt
- Shame
- Lethargic posture and body movements e.g. dragging of feet
- Nothing seems important any more
- Anger
- Loneliness
- Inability to relax
- Feeling that exercise is too difficult
- Disappointment

The Term Depression

Disowning the label

How we view and use the term depression may have an impact on how we experience it. To consider this, let us turn to an analogy.

> Camilla and Lucinda both rented identical cars for a weekend away. On getting her car Camilla decided to personalise it. She bought her favourite lily scented air freshener to hang on the mirror, she arranged some heart shaped cushions on the back seats, she bought a gerbera flower for the dashboard and placed her favourite teddy on the parcel shelf. While she was on holiday she happened to get the car a little muddy and sand from the beach came out of her shoes onto the floor, so she took it to a premium car wash and had it waxed, shined and thoroughly cleaned inside. Lucinda, on the other hand, didn't decorate her car. When it got dirty she remembered that it was a rental car and that the cost of rent included the rental company to clean it on return. After a lovely weekend away, they both took their cars back to the garage. Camilla had to remove her trinkets, her air freshener, teddy and flowers. She found it an emotional experience having to give back the rental car. Lucinda didn't feel that bothered about returning the car.

Why did Camilla find it harder to give back her car? Simply, because she treated it as if it were her own. What relevance does this have to depression you may ask? When I was first diagnosed with depression I used to tell people "I have depression" as though it were something I owned – a possession and a permanent state. Compare the following two phrases:

9

"I am sad" versus "I have sadness"

We don't normally talk about emotions or mental states as though we own them. We would normally say "I am sad", "I'm really happy" etc. Of course, when we have a broken leg we will say "I have a broken leg", but we know it is temporary and we don't view it as something we own.

Over time, I realised that it was unhealthy to say "I have depression" or "I am depressed" because I ended up treating it like I owned it. I had already been defeated by accepting depression as a permanent state. As I began to realise that it was simply a prolonged state of low emotion, I realised there was a better way to view it. I started to say to myself:

I am not depressed.
I am having a moment of depression.

It is more healthy to think of depression as moments of depression – even if they are prolonged and last for months or years.

You will treat a hire car differently to one you own. Do you see depression as something as belonging to you or something you are simply experiencing?

Depression sufferers can be happy
Have you ever seen a depressed person laugh? That doesn't
mean they don't have moments of severe depression or that
they are no longer clinically depressed. It simply means they
have had a short moment of elation and returned to depression
very quickly.

This suggests that a person doesn't own depression as a
permanent state. In this instance their graph would look
something like the following, with a sudden spike at the
moment they laughed at the joke:

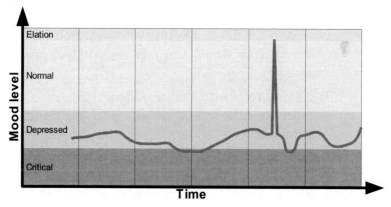

Disowning your depression may be one of the first steps to
recovery. When I say disown, I don't mean to put your head in
the sand, to ignore it, or to blame someone else. I don't want to
hear phrases like "My mother-in-law has lent me her
depression for the weekend" or "I'm renting space in my
mother-in-law's head." I simply mean not seeing yourself as
owning depression. If we begin to own depression, it becomes
part of our identity. We should think of having "moments of
depression" even if they are long uninterrupted periods.

**Don't let depression
become your identity.**

Depression can become a familiar friend

Winston Churchill described his depression as a black dog and sometimes people describe depression as their demons. The individual can become so used to having depression, that it becomes a friend – it becomes ingrained in their identity, and they can't see how they could live without it. The fear of the unknown becomes scarier than having depression so they cling onto it. In effect, they are saying "What would life be like if I wasn't depressed? I'd better keep this thing I own". Some reasons that people may befriend depression and be scared of losing their illness are as follows:

- Your conversations always revolve around your problems. What would you talk about if you weren't depressed?

    1) Firstly, recognise that you don't have to talk in order to make conversation – you can become a good listener.

    2) Secondly, excessive talking about your problems will only contribute to and reinforce negativity. Sometimes you need to give your own ears a rest from your own problems. That doesn't mean ignoring your problems – but there are appropriate times and places to deal with your problems. Airing all your problems to everyone doesn't help the issue.

    3) Thirdly, start learning how to make conversation. That statement might seem like an insult, but a huge majority of adults have difficulty starting and maintaining conversation. Ask some friends how they find starting a conversation in various circumstances and you may be slightly surprised that you are not the only one who finds it difficult.

    Note: Technology and fear may be a contributing

factor to the decline of conversational skills in the twenty-first century.

- You may gain a lot of pity and sympathy from being depressed. People may routinely ask you out to meals or ask if you are okay – and you like this kind of attention. Perhaps you are scared that you wouldn't get this kind of attention if you weren't depressed.

- You feel as though you wouldn't be able to cope if you were well, that you would be forced into work, and you feel that rather daunting.

- Depression can be used as an excuse to avoid things. For example, a depressed person may turn down an invitation to a wedding and say that they suffer from depression. If you didn't have depression, you wouldn't have an excuse to say you didn't want to go.

    The problem here is that socialising may be the thing that is really good for you and if there is a more genuine reason you don't want to attend the event (e.g. not having enough money), then skirting round the issue will become an unhelpful habit. It would be better to say "Sorry I can't come as I don't have the money."

Don't let depression become a friend. I can confidently say life is much more enjoyable when you don't have depression. Listen to people who used to suffer with severe depression, ask them if they would like to go back to it. They won't. Don't resort to thinking you'll always suffer with this. Don't own your depression. Don't underestimate your ability to be happier. You can get better. You can be happy. You can get help. There is hope.

You need to want to get better.
Don't befriend depression.
There is a better way to live.

13

Misdiagnosis

Another problem with the term "Depression" is that it is a vague term; it catches a wide variety of issues. Someone's low mood can stem from a variety of sources. Therefore, it can be difficult to distinguish what the genuine cause is. It's easy to get confused and misdiagnose. For example, the symptoms that are used to diagnose depression are extremely similar to loneliness.

Mildred lived in a large detached house in the countryside. The nearest shops were ten miles away, and she had no neighbours. Sadly she had recently lost her husband. Mildred had never learnt to drive, and so she found herself isolated. With no husband to take her grocery shopping and to her friends in the next village she felt stranded.

It had always been the husband's role to close the main gate, to lock up the house and close the shutters. As she walked to the end of the driveway, the ravens squawking in the treetops would make her feel on edge. Deer suddenly moving in the nearby thicket would make the hairs on her arms stand on end. Her pulse would race.

Without her husband in bed, she would feel anxious and scared. She couldn't sleep and would toss and turn the whole night, listening to every chime of the distant church. Her thoughts would whir, and she constantly told herself how she could not cope without her husband. After a while, Mildred decided to call the doctor. The doctor listened to all her symptoms and decided that she had depression so put her on antidepressants.

All the symptoms that Mildred was facing were to do with losing her husband; her isolation, her fears of being alone. A more correct diagnosis for her should have been loneliness with treatment to improve her social life and help her to consider re-marrying or moving to be nearer friends. What's more, she may now feel guilty for being depressed, or sad to find out she has a medical illness.

There are two ways we can look at her diagnosis:

1. The diagnosis of depression was correct but vague. The main contributing factor to her depression was loneliness.

2. To say she had depression was a misdiagnosis. Her actual problem was loneliness.

The vague diagnosis or misdiagnosis didn't solve the issue and it could have made things worse.

Unfortunately, depression is a broad label that covers a variety of problems. The diagnosis and treatment can become rather impersonal and potentially lead patients and doctors to the wrong conclusions. Obviously, diagnosis is not helped by the fact that doctors are rushed for time.

A correct and specific diagnosis is crucial for being able to recover. If someone struggles with loneliness but has been diagnosed with depression based on the fact that he/she is allergic to gluten, it may send the person on a wild goose chase – which in turn can contribute more to the depression. It is important to pinpoint the **source**, or more likely, **sources** of depression.

When I was first diagnosed with depression I automatically jumped to the conclusion that the problem was a medical physical condition; that there was a lack of serotonin that was getting to the brain and this was causing me to be depressed. This did not leave me much hope. The diagnosis in itself made me depressed. However, in retrospect, I can confidently say

15

that the term "depression" was misleading. Did I have a medical condition? Yes! But was it the **source** of my depression? No! In my case, the physical problems were symptoms of bad thinking rather than the primary source of the problem.

Sadly a lot of people who are diagnosed with depression may jump to the same conclusion as I did. Once you can pinpoint the sources of your depression, it is much easier to recover. This may take some time, as it is like peeling layers off an onion, and sometimes it takes a while to get to the main source of the problem. But it is well worth doing.

Summary

1. Depression is a prolonged sadness where there is little hope for the future accompanied by various negative symptoms

2. Don't treat depression as though you own it. "I am not depressed. I am having moments of depression."

3. Depression can become a familiar friend. Don't let it. "You need to want to get better. Don't befriend depression. There is a better way to live."

4. Depression is a vague diagnosis. You need to find out what the main source of your depression is. There may be more than one contributing factor.

5. Don't jump to the conclusion that depression is necessarily caused by a physical condition. It is possible that changes in the brain may be a result of your thinking.

WHY DO I HAVE DEPRESSION?

Sources

It is important to work out what the source of your depression is. As mentioned previously, there is a tendency to jump to a conclusion that it is simply a physical problem in the brain and the only answer is medication. There are many sources of depression. These can be broadly divided into two areas:

1. **A physical condition or illness:**
   If half of your brain is missing, you have badly hurt your head, you have a brain lesion, you haven't slept in days, or you have a lack of vitamins in your body, these would be considered physical conditions. Your malfunctioning body <u>will</u> affect your thinking.

2. **A mental condition or illness:**
   "Mental" refers to how our minds process events. This is sometimes referred to as cognitive behaviour, or simply how our thoughts work. Circumstances and life can knock us. When someone loses their job, half of the brain doesn't suddenly disappear – they don't suddenly have damage to their skulls. Their reaction to the event will determine whether they become depressed. And because people react differently to the same kind of events, we know it must be the thoughts that determine the results. With a mental condition there is nothing necessarily physically wrong with you. Any chemical changes in your brain may be as a result of your reaction to external circumstances. Mental issues stem from a variety of sources, and these can be divided into two subcategories. Firstly, "Psychological factors": the focus here is how we internally process

events. Secondly, "Social factors": the focus here is more on how external factors can affect us.

Note that these two categories are not mutually exclusive. To recover you need to find the correct sources. It is important to consider the following question:

Is depression a mental or physical illness, or both – if so, which comes first?

Bill had never had a car of his own before, so after he had inherited some money he went out and bought one. He felt proud. He loved the glossy red paintwork, the smell of new upholstery and being able to drive off into the countryside at weekends. Bill was rather too liberal with his use of the accelerator. He would glance in the mirror to check there were no police cars around, crank up the stereo and then zoom along the roads at speeds exceeding 150mph.

In the past, he had always rented cars and never had to worry about topping up the oil and checking the tyres. The months went by and he never maintained the car. One day, as he accelerated along an empty dual carriageway, the smell of oily fumes started wafting through the vents. When the engine started to make grinding noises, he decided he would call into the local garage. The mechanic propped up the bonnet of the car and examined the engine.

"Oh dear," he explained as he glanced across to Bill. "The engine is really in bad shape. It looks like the engine is damaged."

Looking at this scenario do you think:

A) Bill's bad driving and poor maintenance have caused engine damage?

OR

B) A damaged engine has caused Bill to drive badly?

Of course, the answer is A. The engine was not making Bill drive incorrectly, it was the driving that affected the engine. The cause of the problem was the idea that he could continue to drive at 150mph every day and not top up the engine oil.

Our brains are like engines, our thoughts are like driving. In the majority of cases it is our thoughts that cause depression, and these thinking errors express themselves as errors in the brain. However, there are exceptions.

Bill's story is obviously exaggerated to show that driving is the problem. In contrast, there are incidences where an engine, or faulty mechanics, can cause a person to drive badly. Just after university I owned a car and after a while the accelerator developed a fault, where the car would drive itself at 20mph without even putting the accelerator down. My driving was affected by the car's faulty mechanics. A broken accelerator, misaligned steering wheel etc. can affect someone's driving. However, this is seldom the case. It tends to be an exception.

In the majority of cases it is our thoughts (driving) that cause depression. Depression caused by a physical condition (engine problem) is less common. So how do we establish which one it is in any individual case? How do we know whether the driving is the fault and not the engine? Bill's engine problem started months after he had started driving the car. This is strong evidence that Bill's driving was the cause of the problem, not the engine. If it had genuinely been a car fault, this would most likely have been seen from the outset. Likewise, we can look at the timescales and events in someone's life to establish which came first.

The car analogy with Bill emphasises that bad driving causes engine problems – not the other way round. Analogies, however, have their limits. Driving a car well cannot heal a faulty engine. And a good engine can't heal faulty driving. But our brains are different. Good thinking (driving) can actually heal our brains (engine). And a healthy brain (engine) can actually help our thoughts (driving). Neurochemistry affects behaviour, changes in behaviour affect neurochemistry. This is known as "neuroplasticity" and is mentioned in my second book. (The initial draft of this book included more scientific information on depression. However, for most readers this information would not be particularly useful. To make this book more practical I've omitted those chapters and hope to release them later in a separate book).

So returning to our initial question "Is depression a mental or physical illness, or both – if so, which comes first?" In most cases depression is likely to be a mental issue that leads to physical issues – not the other way round. However, because depression can stem from physical conditions we need to assess each individual on a case by case basis.

Blame Games

There is a recent trend to blame depression, negativity or an outlook on life on one's genes, star sign, chemical make-up or character type. As humans we find it easy to pass blame:

"I'm a Virgo, I can't help being depressed."

"My parents both suffered with
depression – it's in my genes."

"I was born with a chemical
imbalance – it's just the way I am."

"If you had a wife like mine, you would be depressed."

However, these blame games don't offer much hope. Blame is about the past. Taking responsibility is about the future. Consider the following:-

A thief runs into a jewellery store, steals a watch and quickly runs out. Who is to blame? Almost certainly the thief. However, if the store owner stands there and keeps telling everyone that he is not to blame, what good does he achieve? Yes the owner may not be to blame, but he still needs to take responsibility; ring the police, report the stolen item etc.

Sometimes it can be difficult to figure out who and what are to blame. Perhaps the owner had been neglectful and forgotten to lock that particular watch away. But trying to figure this out doesn't achieve much. Blame is a waste of energy that could be otherwise diverted into fixing the problem, learning how to cope with the situation, or starting afresh. When we pass blame we admit defeat by saying we'll never get better, we'll never change. This kind of attitude reinforces depression because we won't be able to see a way out.

Blame-shifting is a waste of energy.

Learn to take responsibility for the future.

As I mentioned, in the majority of cases, I believe that it is our driving that ultimately affects our engines, it is our thinking that affects our neurochemistry. In other words, the physical issues are symptoms of depression rather than the cause. It may seem condemning to say that a lot of depression stems from incorrect thinking, but actually it is a relief. If we know

22

that depression results from wrong thinking, then there is hope to get better because we can change our thinking.

Yes it does take a bit of humility and some courage to take responsibility and realise that your thinking and circumstances are the main contributing factor to depression, but it's great news:

You can change your thinking,
but you can't change your genes

You can change your circumstances,
but you can't change your star sign

Depression stems from a variety of sources

Earlier we discussed whether depression is mental or physical. However, we need to be careful that we don't treat these two as mutually exclusive. Depression can stem from a variety of sources. There can be a tendency to over-blame a circumstance or chemical imbalance as the source of one's depression. Even if part of the source of the depression is a physical engine problem, there is probably a large proportion that is also driving related.

> John has been involved in a climbing accident, his head hurts and he feels depressed. The doctor diagnoses that his depression is a result of the fall and he has a chemical imbalance because he has hit his head. He is diagnosed with post-traumatic depression. Every time John meets his friends he tells them that the source of his depression is his climbing accident. However, it is more likely that only a small part of his neurochemistry was affected by the fall and that a large part of his depression is thinking based. John may feel guilty for falling, he may have fears of climbing again, he may have other negative thoughts that are a

reaction to the incident rather than having been caused by the incident. We can see here that he is blaming all of his depression on the accident when actually it is only a part.

Even if depression is biological or genetic, it doesn't mean you can't do anything about it. I believe most depression starts with our lifestyle and how we think about the world around us, our past, present and future. How we feel is primarily determined by how we interpret events (i.e. what we choose to think and believe), and secondly by how we choose to behave. If we can change the way we think, we can change our lives.

"Be careful how you think; your life is shaped by your thoughts." *Solomon 930 BC*

"How you think determines who you are."
Solomon 930 BC

"By changing our thoughts we can change our lives"[1]

There are various sources or contributing factors that lead to depression and these can be divided into the following categories: physical factors, psychological factors and social factors.

Physical Factors

There are many physical factors that can affect depression. Some of these can be the source of depression but it is unlikely they will be solely responsible. They are more likely to be contributing factors and may even be symptoms of depression that stem from other sources.

- Diet – lack of nutrition. Food may be depleted of vital vitamins due to soil quality, ingredients and production quality
- Viruses
- Allergies
- Alcohol – alcohol is a depressant
- Drug abuse
- Seasonal Affective Disorder – the sunshine gives us vital vitamins.
- Lack of exercise
- Excessive noise – noise pollution can contribute to suffering more with depression
- Other physical illnesses
- Music and sound
- Environment
- Light deficiency or excess amounts of high frequency light
- Lack of Sleep / Relaxation
- Low blood sugar
- Dehydration
- Lack of serotonin uptake has been suggested: there is currently little evidence to support this.
- Synapses in the brain fail to function properly
- Memory loss
- Head injuries
- Input and the senses – what we see and listen to affects our minds. So we need to choose these wisely.

Psychological Factors

Much of depression stems from psychological factors. Depression is a wide label that captures a wide variety of thinking issues. The following are the most common contributing factors:

- Anger
- Envy and Comparison
- Lack of Vision
- Shame and Guilt
- Disappointment
- Frustration
- Perfectionism
- Lack of understanding learning curves
- Control seeking
- Fear, Worry and Anxiety
- Sexual issues
- Low self-esteem
- Lack of forgiveness / Bitterness
- Self-punishment
- Work Issues
- Impatience
- Decision-making
- Procrastination
- Unbalanced Perspectives
- Haunting Memories
- Skewed Memories
- Skewed Imagination
- Scepticism rather than Trust
- Lack of Thankfulness
- Unhelpful Perspectives
- Negative Rumination
- Gold digging – putting hope in money
- Fame game – putting hope in being famous

Social Factors

Depression is also largely affected by social factors. The following factors can contribute to depression.

- Loneliness
- Bullying
- Overpopulation
- Globalisation
- Bereavement
- Unemployment
- Social Fears
- Rejection
- How we have been parented

Summary

1. Depression stems from psychological, physical, and social sources

2. Physical problems are more likely to be symptoms rather than causes.

3. Depression does not stem from one source only. Depression stems from multiple sources which can co-exist.

4. Blame games are unhelpful.

HOW DO I RECOVER?

Primary recovery strategies

There are five primary ways you can deal with depression.

1. **Medication**
   Medicating depression can work to a certain extent. Medication can sedate your emotions and thinking so that thoughts are not so intrusive. Even if you believe that depression stems from a physical condition and believe medication is the answer, I would highly recommend applying the other techniques in this list. In doing so, you may lessen the degree to which you suffer and consequently may be able to reduce your intake.

2. **Change your thinking**
   In the majority of cases, depression is caused by psychological factors. By changing your thinking, and learning new cognitive strategies you can become more resilient to depression.

3. **Change your lifestyle**
   If you don't like your job, you have an issue with your circumstances. If you turn up late for work each day, you have an issue with your lifestyle. Your lifestyle is the way in which you approach your circumstances. If your lifestyle is affecting the way you think, then you may need to change your lifestyle.

4. **Change your circumstances**
   Don't underestimate your ability to change your circumstances. It may be that your thinking is largely affected by your circumstances. I now have a job that I enjoy. Don't be deceived, bad company can corrupt character – if you spend a lot of time with negative people you may end up feeling negative.

5. **Reconsider Spirituality**
   You may find that your views on spirituality have a considerable effect on depression. Some spiritual views may bring hope, whilst others may actually contribute to depression. As this is an extensive subject, it is worth considering the topic separately. I may deal with this in a separate book.

Combining Strategies

One of the reasons why people often fail to recover is because they concentrate too much on one strategy. Strategies often need to be combined in order to aid effective recovery.

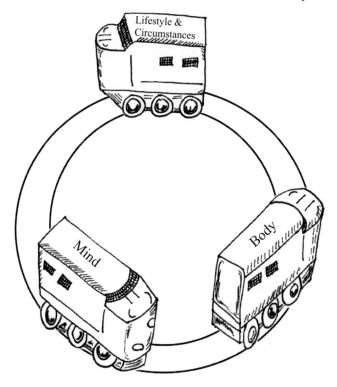

**You need to focus on all the aspects
of depression in order to recover.**

Picture a circular railway track. On it are three trains with words on the top: Body, Mind, Circumstances. These trains have all been derailed and therefore cannot move forward. Let's say we concentrate on getting the "Body" train going. We spend a little while lifting the "Body" train back onto the tracks and getting the engine working. It then starts to move forward. It travels for a little distance and we feel we are getting somewhere. But the next train on the line, the "Mind" train, is still derailed. The "Body" train crashes into it and is derailed again.

This is similar to putting all your efforts into solving your moments of depression by focusing on your diet, sleep, and exercise; and not focusing on your thinking, circumstances or lifestyle. Eventually, you will crash again. In order to get all the trains moving around the circuit, you need to focus on _all_ the aspects of depression.

MEDICATION

There are numerous types of medication on the market. The most common are called serotonin-reuptake inhibitors (SSRI). There is a suggestion that when someone gets depressed the serotonin levels in the brain become depleted causing depression. However, there are psychologists who debunk this as a myth claiming that any benefit is simply due to the placebo effect. Currently there is no evidence to support the theory of chemical imbalance even though this view is widespread; please refer to the section on medicine and science in my second book. In reality, a lot of research is still being done into what really happens to someone's brain when they are depressed. There are a lot of conflicting arguments in the medical world. What's more, pharmaceutical companies really want to promote chemical imbalance as the cause.

SSRI medications have been claimed to increase the levels of serotonin in the brain, which in turn helps to raise one's mood. Doctors tend to medicate these on a trial basis to see which tablets, if any, are effective. Doctors claim that it takes a while for the effects of the medication to kick in, so don't expect overnight changes. Also, please consult a doctor in order to take the medication properly.

My experience of medication was varied. Some tablets seemed to contribute to my putting on weight, which gave me another thing to be depressed about. Some medication actually made me more depressed, some had extreme withdrawal effects, and one seemed to give me a little leg up. At times it was very difficult to work out whether the medication was working because I wasn't using it in isolation; I was also focusing on changing my thoughts.

Problems with medication

Masking Effects

In this section I tackle the problems which can arise when medicating depression. Firstly, I am not endorsing a refusal to take medication for depression, but I believe it is important to warn people of the potential problems.

> Sanjay is running in a marathon and he steps in a pothole. He twists his ankle and he is in a lot of pain. He insists he wants to carry on running in the race, so he takes strong painkillers and applies a cold freeze spray similar to those footballers use. He continues running but the next day his ankle is considerably worse.

We see pain as a negative thing, but the reason Sanjay's leg was in pain was to warn to him to stop running. By masking the pain and keeping on running he is likely to do more damage to himself in the long run. Similarly, if I masked over my fuel gauge light when it turned red and kept driving, I would be heading for bigger problems later on.

So why is this any different with depression? Depression is a mental pain and it is often a warning signal. By taking medication to suppress the symptoms we can sometimes mask the issue and then never really resolve the underlying problem. For instance, if someone is in a bad relationship and gets depressed, that depression may be a warning signal that they need to leave that relationship or make necessary adjustments. By taking antidepressants they may never solve the problem. When taking medication, it is still important to deal with the source. If I put tape over the red fuel gauge, I still need to address the underlying issue that I am running out of petrol.

Depression may be a warning signal telling you that you need to alter your life and your thinking. Medication can simply mask the symptoms and then give you less motivation to make these necessary changes. Because medication "can" work, we can often draw the wrong conclusions.

Just because a solution works, doesn't mean the diagnosis was correct.

Black box testing
In testing computer software there is a method known as "black box testing". The internal structure of the item being tested is not known to the tester. Let's look at a basic example of how black box testing might work with medication:

Stage 1 – Normal Circumstances:
Normal circumstances (i.e. a healthy brain)

Input:
$3 \times 3 + 10$

Output:
19

Stage 2 – Before medication:
Depression circumstances:

Input:
$3 \times 3 + 10$

Output (error):
10!!!

Looking at the above we can see there must be an error in the box i.e. within the brain. Where is the problem in the above scenario? It looks like it could be the initial input. It seems to be missing "3×3" i.e. 9. So let's add 9 to the box in the form of a pill.

Stage 3 – During medication:
Medicating depression circumstances:

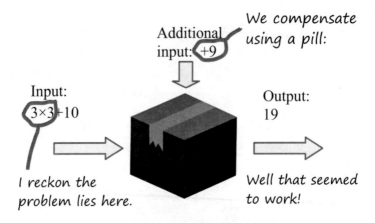

Looking at the above, taking a plus 9 pill appears to work.

Stage 4 – After stopping medication:

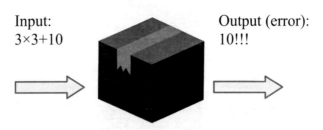

Consider the diagram above. When we stop taking medication, the output returns to 10. From this we conclude that the error must definitely be that the box is deficient of 9; i.e. it is missing the 3×3. In conclusion, we believe that the only solution to fixing the error is the additional input e.g. the plus 9 pill.

The reality:
Now let's open the box:

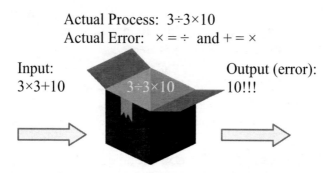

Actual Process: 3÷3×10
Actual Error: × = ÷ and + = ×

Input:
3×3+10

Output (error):
10!!!

Consider the diagram above. In reality, the problem is not a missing 9, it is that there is an error in the reading of the multiplication and addition symbols. When we delve further into the box we find that someone mistyped "×" as "÷" and someone mistyped "+" as "×".

Note that our initial assumption was based on a single error – a missing 9. In reality, there were two problems: a division and a multiplication. Similarly we may jump to wrong conclusions of what happens during depression; often there are multiple problems – these can be referred to as layers.

Masked Layers
The problem with medication is that it can also mask the layers of depression. To explain this let us start with an analogy.

I used to suffer from bad migraines at school and these were most likely due to the fluorescent strip lighting in the classrooms. Fluorescent lights can flicker at a different frequency and can induce headaches. My migraines occurred occasionally. In contrast, consider the following:

> Linda is really sensitive, she gets migraines all the time from the lighting at work. Her headaches are so intense that they last throughout the weekend. She, however, doesn't know that they are induced by the lighting. She goes to the doctor and the doctor prescribes her some medication, telling her she has a chemical imbalance in the brain. She takes the medication and the headache goes away. Several months later, Linda forgets to renew her prescription. She goes to work and after three days of not taking her medication she starts to get headaches again. She now assumes that the cause of her headaches must indeed be the chemical imbalance in the brain because when she stops taking the tablets the problem comes back. However, we know that is not true. We know that it is the lighting that is the source of the problem. The medication is just extremely good at dealing with the symptoms and masking the source of the problem.

Linda's problem can be diagrammatically represented as follows:

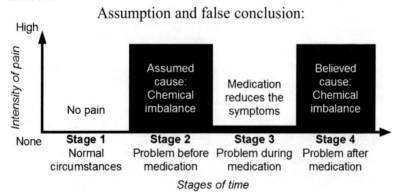

Assumption and false conclusion:

In the graph above the X axis represents the elapsing time with four different stages. Each stage of time is marked and these are similar to the stages in the black box testing. The Y axis represents the intensity of pain. Let's walk through the stages:

- **Stage one:** This shows Linda before she starts getting migraines. The height of the bar chart is 0 and therefore she is feeling no pain.

- **Stage two:** The height of the black box represents the intensity of pain. Linda is in a lot of pain. At this stage the box is still closed, and she and the doctor assume that the cause of these headaches is the result of a chemical imbalance.

- **Stage three:** In stage three Linda takes the medicine based on the assumption made in stage 2. This reduces the pain. A little black bar represents a little amount of pain left despite taking the medication.

- **Stage four:** The pain returns to a high level after Linda stops taking medication. Both Linda and the doctor believe that the cause must be a chemical imbalance. However, in reality, they have drawn a false conclusion. If we open up the boxes, we discover:

In reality:

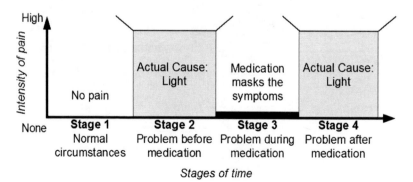

Stages of time

37

The above graph shows the reality of what was happening. The black boxes have been opened, the flaps have been pulled back, and we can see inside. In reality, the light was the issue and the medication had masked the symptoms.

In the above example there is only one cause of the headaches. Let's say Linda also gets headaches from the humming fridge which is next to her desk at work. Both the light and the fridge give a headache of 100% intensity. There is no compound effect happening. Both sources max out her headaches. When the medication is given, it masks the symptoms. Someone then suggests that the light may be inducing her headaches. They exchange the light for a traditional tungsten one and then take her off medication. But she still gets headaches, so they conclude that she does indeed have a medical problem. However, if the fridge also creates the headaches to the maximum level, you can't draw the conclusion that the problem is entirely medical. It could be simply another factor that hasn't been ruled out.

The following diagram shows the assumed cause of the headaches and the false conclusion:

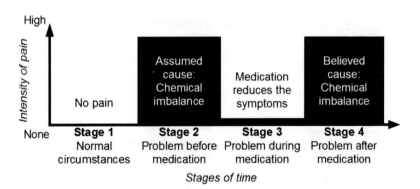

In reality:

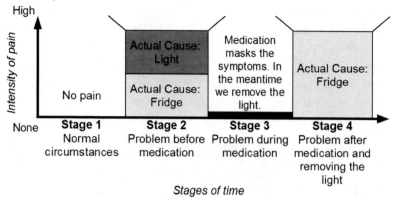

If, on the other hand, Linda's headaches are a result of compounding sources, then, when we remove the light, we would see a reduction in the overall intensity of the headache.

Assumption and partly correct conclusion:

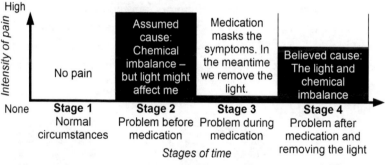

In reality:

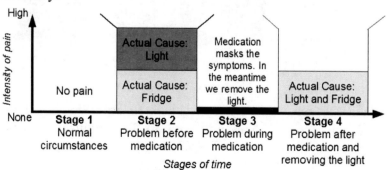

Let's say we explored every single issue and dealt with it. We would find out that not only the light is the cause of the headaches but also the fridge. Then when coming off medication we would have to come to the conclusion that the issue was never a medical imbalance but simply unknown factors. The medication did a good job at dealing with the symptoms but the underlying issue was never a medical one.

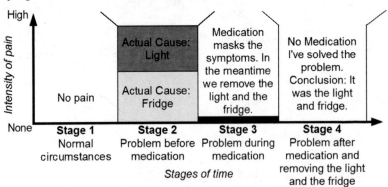

Medication can mask several layers and lead you to believe that there is only one layer. Let's say someone is diagnosed with depression. The actual cause is unknown but the assumption is that the depression is caused by a faulty immune system:

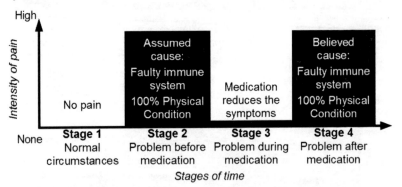

When the medication period comes to an end and all the symptoms return it is easy to jump to the conclusion that the depression must stem from the faulty immune system. However, in reality, it could be that the medication is just

40

extremely good at masking the symptoms from other causes of depression. In reality, the depression may look more like the following:

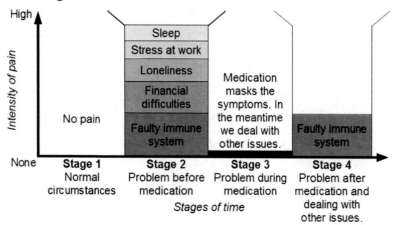

How can you discern whether your depression is 100% a physical condition? It's almost impossible to. The only way to find that out is to start eliminating the other layers. In reality, I believe that most depression is layer based; with the majority of symptoms stemming from cognitive (thinking) issues. I would strongly recommend dealing with all layers even if your diagnosis is a physical condition. It may be that by dealing with other layers you can reduce the overall level of depression to the point where drugs can be reduced. People who suffer with faulty immune systems would strongly benefit from cognitive help anyway, as it builds character and self-awareness.

> **It's almost impossible to prove that your moments of depression are 100% a physical condition because there are so many layers. The only way to find out is to deal with the other layers.**

If you manage to get your medication down, that is great, because medication can have some rather horrible side effects.

Side Effects

Medication comes with a variety of side effects that may hinder recovery. In particular, a decreased attention span and lethargy. These side effects make it harder to consider and make vital adjustments to one's lifestyle and circumstances. Besides lethargy, antidepressants are known to increase weight and affect diet. This is because the highest levels of serotonin in the body are found in the stomach, and pills can upset the natural balance. Some medicines have worsened depression and others can be linked to memory loss. For these reasons, be cautious when taking medicine. If you already happen to be on medication, please don't suddenly stop. Going cold turkey on antidepressants has led people to suicide. So please make sure medication is properly supervised.

For me, the side effects of medication outweighed any benefits. Exercise has been much more beneficial than medication – but I'm not you. Please consult your doctor.

Summary

1. Medication *may* help with depression by giving you a leg up.

2. It is not good to become overdependent on medication.

3. Medication *may* help get rid of the symptoms.

4. Medication can mask the true source of your problems, so it is important to deal with the psychological aspects even if the medication is working.

5. Medication can mask various layers leading people to the wrong conclusions.

6. Depression is often based on a variety of sources.

7. Medication can have some undesirable side effects.

CHANGE YOUR THINKING PART 1

INSTILLING HOPE

Replacement Theory

In recent years many books have been released on how to treat depression, and yet many people still struggle with it. One of the main reasons I believe that people struggle to deal with their depression is that they are tackling it in the wrong way – they are trying to get rid of depression rather than instilling hope.

Imagine some ping-pong balls in a high-ball glass. Each of these ping-pong balls represents an element of depression. On one ping-pong ball is written worry, another guilt. If you try to dig them out with a fork, it can be difficult. An easier way to get them out is simply to pour water into the glass. They will then float to the surface and fall out.

Likewise, it is much easier to deal with depression by pouring in hope than trying to get rid of depression. In other words, we displace depression with hope. Hope is the opposite of depression. Hope is defined as:

The positive expectation of good

All the psychological factors listed earlier in this book steal hope. As we deal with each of them in turn, we will not focus so much on how to get rid of them but simply focus on the antidote. An antidote is really important. Let's go back to the analogy of digging the ping-pong balls out. If you successfully removed the balls with a fork, you'd be left with an empty glass and the worry and guilt balls could easily be put back in the glass. Once it is full of water it is much harder to put back the worry and guilt balls.

Likewise, if you simply get rid of depression you can end up with a gaping hole that can easily be filled with the same problems. By filling the mind and heart with hope you protect yourself from the balls of depression re-entering.

**Rather than root out depression,
we should try to instil hope.**

Be Specific

In order to find hope we need to be specific. If your depression is stemming from worry, then you need to deal with the specific worries.

> Bob works in a shop. He believes that 2+2=5. His boss keeps asking him to count the money in the till at the end of the day but Bob keeps making a mistake. Bob has now been threatened by his boss that he will lose his job if he continues to make mistakes. Bob asks his friends for advice. Some friends tell him to stop worrying about losing his job. Some of his friends tell him to believe he can do it; that if he makes a mistake, it isn't the end of the world. When Bob goes back to work, he miscounts the money in the till and loses his job.

44

What Bob's friends told him didn't solve the problem. If anything they may have made things worse because now, not only has Bob lost his job, but he now has lost trust in his friends; he may believe that his friends don't love him. Note that his friends stated a general truth "The world isn't going to end", but this general truth does not set Bob free of his problem. He needs a specific answer to a specific problem. He needs to be told that 2+2=4.

In any given situation there is a specific truth that will help alleviate a problem. In order to bring hope, specific help needs to be given, rather than general answers.

Hope is specific

Will Power is not the answer – Truth is
In the story of Bob you may have also noticed that his friends told him to "Stop worrying." What did it achieve? Little. That is because will power cannot alone solve problems. Neither can strong belief. Bob could have thought "I can do this" and tried to boost himself with confidence and belief in himself. He could have constantly told himself not to worry about the outcome – but the only thing that could set him free of the problem at hand was the truth that 2+2=4.

You cannot tell someone to be more compassionate. You cannot tell someone to stop being disappointed. You cannot tell someone to stop being envious. You need to tell them a specific truth to solve the problem.

Another example might be with a negative obsessive thought such as "I'm a failure." By telling someone to stop thinking that, you leave the glass empty, and the balls (obsessive thoughts) have easy access to come back again. Will power cannot suppress obsessive thoughts. The more you try not to think of being a failure the more you think of being a failure.

The person needs to be told that they are "not a failure," told that they "are a success." Have it explained to them until it makes sense.

You don't get rid of negative thoughts by refusing to think about them. You have to substitute them with truth until they disappear. In other words, memories are generally replaced, not forgotten. This is mentioned in my second book on memory and science.

Bad memories need to be replaced.

Sometimes we have depression but can't put our finger on why we are depressed, and sometimes we can put our finger on the problems but can't think of the answer. Hopefully, this book will highlight some areas of your thought-life and give you answers. You may need to spend a bit of time locating problems and finding solutions. But it is worth it in the end.

Truth restores hope.

Facing the Truth

Often we need to seek the truth not the cause of the problem. Sometimes we can end up focusing on how we came to believe something. We may try to find out where our thoughts came from. We may spend ages trying to place blame on someone else for why we find ourselves in this situation. The problem is that it is difficult, nearly impossible, to work out where a problem stemmed from. We can tire ourselves out going round in circles. It is far better to focus on the antidote than on the cause of the problem.

Focus on the antidote,
not the problem.

Sometimes we find it hard to face the truth. Let's say we were bullied at school so badly that we couldn't concentrate on our studies and ended up with poor grades. We could focus on blaming the bullies for the poor grades and for now feeling a failure, or we could focus on the antidote – how to become a success going forward. Just like the glass analogy we should focus on instilling hope – not getting rid of problems.

It is really important to focus on hope.

At times it can be hard to face the truth. Yes – perhaps I'm depressed because I made bad choices in life. Perhaps I have depression from being severely in debt. Yes – it does take a bit of humility and some courage to take responsibility and realise that you've made a mistake. People make mistakes, but don't focus on the mistake – focus on the antidote.

Hope and Truth Grow

Hope is not instant, you grow in hope. Truth isn't instant, you grow in truth. Self-awareness is not instant, you grow in self-awareness. Depression is often caused by what we believe. There is a saying that "The truth sets us free", however, this is not entirely accurate. We need to know the truth, then we need to continue to remember it by choosing to live and practise it. It must become heart knowledge not just head knowledge.

Let's say the following happened:
1. We tell Bob "2+2=4".
2. He writes it down on a piece of paper.
3. At home he reads the paper several times.
4. The next day he completely forgets that "2+2=4" and counts the till using his old truth "2+2=5"

In the above scenario Bob would still achieve the same results. He would still lose his job. For this reason, it is vital head knowledge becomes heart knowledge.

47

From head to heart

The problem with knowledge is that sometimes you "know" in your mind the answers but you don't live up to this knowledge. For example, you may know that driving over the speed-limit is putting both others' and your own life at risk, potentially leading to a speeding fine, and less economical for your wallet. However, you may still continue to speed. Why?

This is often because you have either forgotten this knowledge or because it is head knowledge rather than heart knowledge. Even reminders can soon fade and merge into the background. You might see a speeding sign but not even think about it – it becomes part of the wallpaper of life.

In order to transfer knowledge from your head to your heart, I have found this ancient saying useful.

**"Remember this. Keep it in mind.
Take it to heart."[2]**

Repetition is also key. Just like practising a piece of music, meditation on a positive thought will move the thought from your head to your heart.

Truth and hope protect

As we learn truths, it is like collecting shields in a game. Each shield is used to protect us from a particular arrow. The red shield is used to protect us from the red arrow. The blue shield from the blue arrow. A problem I often face is that even though I have the shield, I haven't yet developed quick enough reflexes. The enemy shoots a red arrow, but my red shield is on the ground. I'm slow to pick it up, and by the time I have, the red arrow has already hit me; so I need to spend ages in pain taking out the arrow and waiting for the wound to heal. If I was quicker with my reflex actions, I would be able to stop the red arrow hitting me in the first place.

Mentally it is the same. First, we need to have a shield ready to defend ourselves, and then we need to develop mental reflexes to deal with the situation quickly before we get hurt.

For example, if one evening someone comes up to me and says "You're a failure because you aren't a millionaire". If I don't have a shield I may fall for that – agree with it and let the arrow bury deep into my heart. I may even agree with them, which is like pushing the arrow further into my body.

I may have a truth at the back of my mind, such as "You don't need to be rich in order to be happy", but if my reflexes are slow and I don't think of that truth until the next morning, that is like spending ages looking for the shield before picking it up. I've already spent a whole evening having been hurt by that arrow.

If I have practised that truth a lot, it is like building a reflex muscle. When the person says the lie, I can pull up the shield of truth quickly to defend myself. We need to practise the truth so that our reflexes are fast.

Build Strong Mental Reflexes

Creativity reinforces hope and truth

Writing a book about depression is, in itself, helping me. This is because, as I am writing, I am constantly reinforcing the truth in my head and building my mental reflexes.

One way to get thoughts from your head to your heart is to use metaphor, stories and pictures. Aristotle suggested that the use of narrative was key to ingraining a thought in the memory. We easily remember stories, because they apply to the senses and imagination. If I tell someone not to forget their keys each time they leave the house, they may forget that. If I tell them a story about how I once left my house and forgot my keys, they will most likely remember the story and its associations, and this will help to get the idea of remembering their keys from their head to their heart. It is much easier to understand, perceive and remember something when expressed in metaphor or parable.

By writing poetry or books, associating truths to pictures etc. it is easier to build your mental reflexes. By making a film and creating analogies I believe I am instilling the truths better in my head. Making a film about depression has largely benefited me for this reason.

Creativity helps build strong mental reflexes.

Another important principle of getting information from your head to your heart is to learn the answers of life for yourself. If a teacher simply gave answers to the students at school when they had a test, the students would never learn the answers for themselves, and, as a result, would not be so well equipped. Some wisdom is required here; however, I don't mean you should put yourself through problems just to find answers. Ideally, we should learn from others.

Some memory strategies

How to remember is a large topic in itself. Strategies may differ from individual to individual, but some general principles can be applied to remembering the truth:

- Highlight truths you find in books.
- Reread and repeat truths often.
- Write down the truths.
- Use post-it notes around the house.
- Find bite-size statements, idioms or proverbs that remind you of the truth.
- Associate a truth with something you already know.
- Vary the reminders.
- Set aside time to mull over positive thoughts.
- Get creative – draw visual reminders.
- Link a truth to a picture – e.g. a rose might mean "My friends accept me.".
- Link a truth to a sound – e.g. the sound of a bell might mean "I have loving parents".
- Create your own analogies and stories to help you remember things.
- Use positive songs to reinforce positive thoughts.
- Avoid negativity.
- Repetition is key.
- Make learning the truth fun.
- Study with someone else so you can remind each other.
- Learn the truths in the same situation and location you are likely to need them. For example, "Rehearsing the highway code will be more effective when you are in a car, than when you are in classroom."

Acting

Another way to get a truth from our head to our heart is to act it out. To a certain degree, you can act your way into being happier. Studying acting techniques may help to alleviate low mood. I found reading Stanislavski and other acting books useful in learning how to change my mood. You may think this is putting on a mask or that you are just pretending, but actually when we do pretend this in turn genuinely induces feelings of happiness. The reverse is true, we can act depressed and consequently we will feel more depressed.

If you could ask an Oscar winner who has just acted out a depressing scene how they feel – they will say they actually feel depressed. Likewise, if an actor has just acted out a happy scene they are more likely to feel happy. You should act what you want to believe and feel, even if you don't believe and feel it. However, please note that emotions and feelings often take time to catch up with any new beliefs. This is known as "the lag of emotions".

Try listening to a piece of happy upbeat music. I want you to listen to it once and then on the second time, hum or whistle along. How do you feel afterwards - a little more upbeat? That is because you are acting happy and it is actually influencing your general mood.

Some suggestions are as follows:
- Katrina & The Waves – Walking on Sunshine
- Queen – Don't Stop Me Now
- Village People - YMCA
- Mozart – Marriage of Figaro Overture
- John Williams – Raiders March from Raiders of the Lost Ark
- Sebastion Cabot & Phil Harris – The Bare Necessities from the Jungle Book

The Label of Depression

To a certain extent, we act what we believe. We mentioned earlier that one of the problems with the saying "I am depressed" or "I have depression" is that it suggests a permanent state. This can potentially lead people to act more depressed than they really are. For instance, if you tell people that you've been signed off work with depression, you may feel that you have to live up to that diagnosis. You could refrain from laughing at a joke; fearing that if you did, others would believe that you lied about your diagnosis.

The label of "Depression" can make you act more depressed.

I remember a time when I was generally depressed but on one particular day, I felt quite happy. Later that day I found myself surrounded with people who I had previously told I had depression. I now felt as though I had to act depressed otherwise I wasn't living up to my diagnosis. If someone made a joke, I felt as though I shouldn't laugh because I had depression. This kind of acting probably stemmed from the fear that people wouldn't take my depression seriously and would talk behind my back saying things like "He's not really depressed, I saw him laughing the other day." I believed and had assumed that if someone was diagnosed with depression they would be depressed all the time and wouldn't have moments of happiness. My beliefs resulted in me acting more depressed than I was, and that, in turn, actually made me more depressed. My assumption of how others would judge me affected my behaviour.

Being labelled as depressed or having depression is unhelpful because sometimes the person feels they need to live up to that new label, that they are 100% depressed. It's okay to have moments of happiness even if you've been signed off work with depression. It is important to understand this otherwise you can end up acting depressed to keep in-line with your diagnosis and this can, in turn, lead to longer and more intense periods of depression, because your feelings can be manipulated by acting.

Even if it is only to a small degree, acting depressed will in turn make you more depressed. To emphasise the point I mentioned earlier in the book, it would be better to tell people you have "moments of depression".

Interestingly, having written a book and made a film about depression, I sometimes feel that I must live up to the expectation of never being depressed (which might sound like I'm wearing a mask or pretending). However, acting accordingly has actually led me to suffer fewer episodes of depression.

If you act as though you are depressed, then you'll end up more depressed.

If you act as though you are not depressed, depression will be alleviated to a certain extent.

Act despite what you feel
To act as though something is true is not living in denial, ignoring your problem or wearing a mask. First, you acknowledge your problem, then you act upon how you want to be in the future.

Nathan is not a generous person and doesn't feel generous. He wants to be a generous person but every time he is given an opportunity to be generous he says, "Sorry. I'm not a generous person. I don't feel generous today." That will only reinforce his lack of generosity. If he says "I want to be a generous person, I don't feel generous, but I am going to give you some money", then as he starts to practise generosity he will start to feel generous. The fact is, your feelings do not <u>always</u> reflect the truth. Feelings can deceive us. For example:

> Joe tells Sandra that her cat has died; he saw it in the road.
> Sandra bursts out in tears. She feels low and sad.
> Ten minutes later Sandra's cat walks in.
> Joe must have seen a different cat that looked liked Sandra's.

The feelings of sadness that Sandra had for the first 10 minutes were real to her. But her feelings did not reflect the reality of the situation. Her cat was not dead. In this way, feelings are real, but they do not always reflect the reality of the situation. Feelings don't always reflect objective truth, only what we believe to be true. Because of this, emotions are not always reliable. We shouldn't <u>*always*</u> trust our feelings.

Feelings are real, but they do not always reflect the reality of the situation.

If we act on our feelings, we <u>*can*</u> end up being an emotional yo-yo. If you wait until you feel like doing something, you may never do it. So sometimes we need to act contrary to our emotions. We should act as though something is true and as we do so, our emotions will catch up.

One of the most powerful emotions that keeps us from acting is fear. If we are always bound by fear, we will never do anything. Dale Carnegie writes about this in his book about public speaking:

> "He says that at the outset almost every man is frightened when he goes into action, but that the course to follow is for the man to keep such a grip

on himself that he can act just as if he were not frightened. After this is kept up long enough, it changes from pretence to reality, and the man does in very fact become fearless by sheer dint of practising fearlessness when he does not feel it.

This was the theory upon which I went. There were all kinds of things of which I was afraid at first, ranging from grizzly bears to 'mean' horse and gun-fighters; but by acting as if I were not afraid I gradually ceased to be afraid. Most men can have the same experience if they choose."[3]

Act despite what you believe

Not only do we sometimes have to act despite our feelings, but sometimes we have to act despite our beliefs.

Boris is in a walking group but he hates rope bridges. He comes to a rope bridge across a cavern. The twenty people in front of him cross the bridge. Boris has feelings of nervousness, and he also believes the rope will snap. Everyone insists that it is safe. If Boris waits until his feelings subside, he'll never likely cross. If he waits until he believes the bridge is safe, he'll also never cross. He realises that he needs to believe the rope is safe. He is trying to rid his old belief that "all rope bridges are unsafe" and adopt the new belief that "if everyone else can cross, then so can I". However, he can't seem to get rid of his old belief. What he needs to do is act according to the new belief he wants to adopt. As he acts, steps on and crosses the bridge, he will confirm that his new beliefs are true.

**Not only should we act despite our feelings,
but we should act according to the new
beliefs we want to adopt.**

56

If we change our behaviour, our beliefs will follow. It takes time to re-educate the mind, but it doesn't take time to change our behaviour, which actually facilitates the process of re-educating our minds, as well as positively affecting how we feel. You may want to ask yourself:

How would I behave if I truly believed this?

One way we can act our way into new behaviour is to schedule the use of our time. It's good to schedule events and activities that get you out of your negative mood. Work even if you don't feel like it. Plan an activity and stick to it. Sometimes we have to work through the pain.

I remember a time when I felt exceptionally low. I was due to teach English that day. I felt like cancelling, ringing in sick. Did I feel like teaching? No. Did I feel ready and prepared to teach? No. However, I knew teaching would do me good as I would have to act normal. I couldn't stand in front of a class and mumble at them. It would be rather bad for the students if I stood there down in the mouth. So I went to work and tried to act as though I was happy. Even when I was acting happy, confident and prepared I didn't feel like it. However, by the end of the day, my mood had significantly lifted – simply because to a certain extent you can act your way into a better mood. Acting helps to get head knowledge into your heart, emotions and reality.

You can act and speak hopefully even if you don't feel like it, and that will, in turn, instil hope.

Summary

1. Rather than trying to get rid of depression it is better to instil hope.

2. Find specific answers to specific problems.

3. Will power does not solve our problems, truth does.

4. Facing the truth can be difficult.

5. Hope and truth take time to develop. Don't expect overnight wonders.

6. You need to get knowledge from your head to your heart in order for it to be effective.

7. Metaphor, stories and pictures help us to remember.

8. The use of our memories is key to instilling and maintaining hope.

9. To a certain extent, we can act our way out of depression.

10. Don't label yourself as depressed.

11. Act despite what you feel.

12. Act in accordance with the beliefs you want to adopt.

CHANGE YOUR LIFESTYLE

Lifestyle is defined as: "The way in which a person lives"[4]. If I change my *job*, I change my *circumstances*. If I change my *thoughts at work*, I change my *thinking*. If I change my *arrival time*, such as getting to work earlier, I change my *lifestyle*.

Job	(circumstance)
Thoughts at work	(thinking)
Arrival time	(lifestyle)

Changing your lifestyle is an important factor when recovering from depression. Even if you can't change your circumstances, it may be possible to change your lifestyle.

**Don't underestimate your ability
to change your lifestyle.**

Tiredness and Energy

Tiredness is one of the biggest factors in depression. Tiredness can steal hope and lead to depression. When we are tired both our physical and mental defences are down. Our brains function differently. When we are tired the amygdala (region of the brain which controls emotion) can overreact to negative stimuli.[5] Because of this, we become more susceptible to anger, guilt, worry, disappointment and other negative emotions.

Hope creates energy

Tiredness can lower our levels of hope. However, thankfully the reverse is true: Hope can increase energy. Consider the following:

Lucy has felt tired all day; her friend asks her if she wants to go for a walk in the park, or shopping, but Lucy complains that she doesn't have enough energy. Later that day another friend rings her to tell her that her favourite pop star is in the local bookshop signing autographs and will only be there for another half-an-hour. Lucy doesn't even think about having a lack of energy, she is up off the couch in seconds and walks briskly to the bookshop to meet her favourite star.

Where did Lucy suddenly get all that energy from? She got it from a sudden burst of hope. The hope of seeing her favourite pop star energised her enough to be able to walk to the bookshop. If your house was on fire, would you sit there and say "Well, I don't have enough energy to leave". It's amazing how people who have hope can suddenly find relief from their symptoms of pain, or find the energy to do something they thought they were incapable of.

In Lucy's case, she actually had more physical energy than she realised.

Hope can increase energy.

**You have more energy than you realise,
even if you don't feel it.**

Tiredness is often psychological
There are two types of tiredness "psychological (mental)" and "physical". Often we can confuse these because they are closely linked.

If we are mentally tired, that will affect our physical energy. If we are physically tired, it can affect our mental energy. For this reason, constant rumination about tiredness, such as telling yourself you are tired all the time, will actually make yourself feel more tired. But in reverse, you can make yourself more energetic, by telling yourself that you do have energy. Positive thoughts create energy. In particular, an attitude of gratitude leads to higher energy levels.[6]

Thankfulness increases energy levels

Because tiredness is such a big factor during depression we need to make sure our sleeping habits are healthy.

Sleep

Probably one of the biggest lifestyle factors in depression is your sleeping habits; the amount of sleep you have, the quality of sleep and the times at which you sleep. Depression can lead to sleeping problems and sleeping problems can lead to depression, so it can be a bit of a vicious cycle.

Lack of sleep can lead to tiredness. As mentioned in the previous section, tiredness can steal hope. Tiredness affects our emotions and can lead to poor memory function. Having healthy functioning memories is key to maintaining good mental health. Memories are consolidated during sleep, and therefore good quality sleep is absolutely vital.

Lack of sleep can also affect our physical health. With good sleep, a cut normally takes a couple of days to heal, but without proper sleep, it can take several weeks. If we are to stay happy, we need to focus on maintaining good physical health too.

In addition, lack of sleep can also lead to obesity. This is because lack of sleep leads to increased levels of the ghrelin hormone and a decreased level of leptin, leaving you feeling hungry. If you can't seem to get your energy from sleep, your body will try to get it from food. Unfortunately, when we try to get energy from food, which should have been gained through sleep, it leads to putting on weight. So if you are constantly hungry and eating, it might be a sign that you are not sleeping properly.

We can see here that healthy sleep is absolutely vital to all areas of life. However, sadly many people in western culture have poor sleeping habits.[7]

Physical Tiredness

Sleep relies heavily on us being "physically" tired. When we get mentally tired we can _feel_ physically tired, even if our actual physical levels are high. Because of this, it is important to make sure we exercise during the day, so that we can fall and stay asleep at night.

Ellie has had a stressful day and has been angry. She feels tired but can't get to sleep. Yes, Ellie is "psychologically" tired, but she is not "physically" tired enough to sleep. She would benefit from doing some physical exercise.

If you are mentally exhausted, it is good to examine yourself and see if you've done enough exercise that day. If you haven't had much physical exercise, it can be of great benefit to force yourself past the "psychological" tiredness and do 30 minutes of exercise. In the long run, you will sleep better and feel more emotionally and physically refreshed in the morning.

Mental worries

Tiredness doesn't always mean we will sleep. In fact, mental tiredness will often keep us awake. Worry is the biggest stealer of sleep, so dealing with our thought life is crucial to sleep. Hopefully other sections of this book will help you here. One of the most useful is to write down your worries before you climb into bed.

Length in Bed
During sleep we go through various stages; these are referred to as cycles. Typically a cycle will last 1.5 hours, and we need approximately 5 of these cycles to function well – a total of 7.5 hours sleep per night. We don't tend to fall asleep immediately and occasionally wake between these cycles; that is why 8-9 hours in bed is the recommended time. Ideally, you want to keep a regular schedule where you go to bed at the same time and get up at the same time each day.

Snoozing
Snoozing and staying in bed too long is actually very bad for mental health.[8] By staying in bed longer you would think that it would allow your body to have more rest and sleep. However, in reality, the amount of sleep you have is just spread across the time you spend in bed. If you spend 10 hours in bed as opposed to 8, all your body will do is spread out that sleep across those 10 hours leading to less efficient sleep. The amount of sleep you need is like a certain amount of butter. You can spread butter thickly on a small piece of toast, or the same amount of butter thinly a large piece of toast. By staying in bed for 10-12 hours all you are doing is damaging the efficiency of your sleep.

Snoozing in itself causes problems because cycles are typically 1.5 hours long. If you fall asleep for another 10 minutes, you will be waking up mid-cycle, causing you to feel even more groggy. So getting out of bed when you wake is helpful. If you are anything like me, that can still be difficult. I have a tendency to try and solve all my problems lying in bed. Firstly, you are not going to solve all your problems in one go, and, secondly, lying in bed is probably the worst place to solve problems; we are much more effective at solving problems when we are physically active – for example during walking.

**You are not going to solve all your problems
lying in bed. So get up and get on with your day.**

If you fail to sleep it is still better to get up and get on with your day. There are many famous people who suffered from insomnia: Napoleon Bonaparte, Abraham Lincoln, Madonna, Lady Gaga, to name a few. Many Olympic athletes also claim that they fail to sleep the night before they have to compete. Your body is quite capable of dealing with a lack of sleep, as long as it's not regular. So don't beat yourself up if you can't sleep – you'll handle it.

Even if you fail to get sleep,
you can still be productive.

You are still valuable and can make
a difference to other people's lives
even if you have slept poorly.

Lifestyle habits can severely affect our levels of tiredness. The following are some suggestions for improving sleep:-

- Refrain from using smartphones or laptops before bedtime. Staring at a smartphone for half-an-hour is like staring at a light bulb for five minutes. It stimulates the brain rather than allowing it to relax.
- When using smartphones or laptops adjust the screen brightness down so that it is not so tiring on the eyes. Install a colour altering app such as F.lux or Twilight.
- Use dimmed, orange, or soft lights to help you relax before you go to bed.
- Read a fiction book to take your mind off your worries and work.
- Do not eat after 7pm. Eating late can affect your ability to sleep.
- Avoid caffeine in the evening. It takes about 4-6 hours for it to completely remove from your system.
- Exercise is important in improving your sleep, but

excessive exercise just before bed can keep you awake.

- Keep your bedroom cool. Cooler temperatures help us to fall asleep quicker.

- Put a pillow between your knees as this will create better alignment of the spine.

- Make sure you are hydrated before you go to bed, but don't drink too much as you will need to go to the toilet during the night,

- Get plenty of sun during the day.

- Eat more vegetables, fruit, and fish as these promote good sleep. Avoid junk food.

- Avoid alcohol or illegal drugs before bed. You may feel that they help you get to sleep quicker, but the quality of sleep will be reduced.

- Take a nap during the day but not too late – between 1pm and 3pm is a good time. A nap should ideally be no longer than 20 minutes - if it is longer, it will disturb your circadian rhythm leading to you having less sleep at night.

- Deal with your worries – hopefully the section on worries will give you some help.

- Drink hot milk or honey before bedtime, as studies show that these can make you feel sleepier.

- Try reverse psychology. If you tell yourself that you don't want to get to sleep and try to force to keep your eyes open, it can make you fall asleep faster.

- Try the 4-7-8 technique. Inhale through your nose for 4 seconds, hold your breath for 7 seconds, and then exhale through your mouth for 8 seconds. Repeat this until you fall asleep.

- There are various sleep apps and alarms available for smartphones that may help in promoting healthy sleep.

- Read books on how to sleep better.

As an extra thought, when sleeping we all dream. These dreams are an important part of processing our desires and worries. It can be interesting to note down your dreams as they may tell you things about yourself you weren't aware of. They may highlight fears and desires that are not so apparent to you during waking hours.

Sleep is vital for good mental health

Music, Sound and Noise

Music Choice

Lifestyle choices we make can have a profound effect on our mental health. Music has a strong ability to change our emotions and at times can literally manipulate them. Francis Ford Copolla and Spielberg have played music on film sets just before filming a scene to get actors in the mood.[9] Film composers know how to manipulate your emotions, to make you feel more tense or relaxed. For this reason, it is important to choose music wisely. Is the music having a positive or negative effect on your emotions?

I personally love classical music, but in recent years, I've become much more aware of how different pieces affect my emotions. I listen to a lot more Mozart and calm music than I used to and if I listen to sad music, I limit myself to a certain amount of time.

Music Associations

We also need to be aware of any associations that are linked to the music we listen to. Music can paint pictures in our minds. What happens when you hear Star Wars playing? You probably picture a spaceship crossing the sky. What happens when I hear the opening of Sibelius's second symphony? I picture pebbles bouncing across a lake. However, music can also paint negative pictures and recall negative associations.

If you happened to have a traumatic experience, let's say a divorce, whilst listening to a particular piece of music, it may be that when you hear that music it wells up emotions and thoughts associated with that experience. Every time I listen to Finzi's clarinet concerto it reminds me of unrequited love, and if I'm not careful I can fall into negative rumination. Does that mean I shouldn't listen to it - not exactly - more that I need to carefully guard my thoughts when I listen to it. After all, it's a wonderful piece of music.

Actively Listen

Music is also a useful tool for drowning out negative rumination because it helps us to focus on the present. However, the problem is that music can often become background sound rather than something we actively listen to. Studying music, even if learning to recognise different sounds, can encourage you to actively listen to music. You may have to remove distractions so you can properly listen and concentrate on the music. I like to find a quiet place to lie down and close my eyes, so I can fully concentrate on the music.

Choose Lyrics Wisely

You may also need to consider the lyrics in songs. Are the lyrics full of negativity or are they positive lyrics?

> Barry was single and struggled with being single. He often told me that he was sexually frustrated and used to get angry and depressed about it. However, on observing his music choice I discovered that he used to constantly listen to songs about sex and love. No wonder he was constantly sexually frustrated, no wonder he was fed up with being single. He was constantly reminding himself via music. His songs were augmenting his own negative rumination.

Active music making

You don't have to necessarily be musically gifted to become involved in music making. Not only does it give you an opportunity to make new friends but it can help alleviate low mood. I highly recommend singing as a therapy for depression. If you join an amateur choir or sing in a group, such as a church gathering, you don't need to worry about your voice because you probably won't stand out, people most likely won't hear you. Filling your lungs with air and singing also sends endorphins around your body. A good sing is the equivalent of a good workout. Find a local choir and give it a go. Give it at least three weeks trial to allow the initial fears to subside.

Find Relaxing Sounds

Not only can music manipulate our emotions, but sound can also have an impact on our emotions. Film-makers use sound effects to create tension, relaxation etc. Sound is often based on association. What do you associate with the sound of church bells? What picture does it paint in your mind? What do you associate with the sound of a creaking door? What picture does that paint in your mind?

What is your favourite colour? You've probably thought of that one. But have you ever asked yourself what your favourite sound is? Probably not.

Certain sounds can make us more relaxed. Sounds from nature such as birdsong, the sea etc. may help to alleviate low mood. There are free sounds available on the internet. You can download them and use them as ring-tones, or simply listen to them. Explore listening to various sounds and discover what you find relaxing.

Avoid Excessive Noise

When Hitchcock made his films he would sometimes include certain sounds and frequencies in order to make the audience feel anxious, nauseous or tense.[10] If we are constantly bombarded with lots of noise it can agitate our emotions, disturb sleep and relaxation. Statistics show that people who live in cities are more prone to depression.[11] Whilst there are many other potential factors involved, one may be that those people are exposed to more noise pollution.

Become aware of what sounds agitate you. It might be subtle and affect you slowly over time. My parents' television used to make a high-pitched whine when left on standby mode. I became aware that if it was left on for long periods of time whilst I was in their lounge, it would start to affect my emotions.

Alcohol and Drugs

Alcohol is a depressant and should be carefully monitored when you are depressed. Ideally, it should be completely avoided. If you do drink alcohol, it is best to reserve it for Friday or Saturday evening when you are more relaxed. You need to be careful with the amount you drink. If you can't control your intake, it may be best not to start. It is best to avoid drinking on your own, as people tend to drink quicker when their pace is not moderated by other drinkers.

If you are on medication, alcohol should be especially avoided. Alcohol can negate the effects of the medication, and in some cases can make issues worse. In my experience, I've met a lot of people prescribed with antidepressants who continue to drink.

The biggest show-stopper for me when it comes to alcohol is how it affects sleep. Alcohol allows one to fall asleep quicker but it seriously affects the quality of one's sleep. The sleep for the rest of the night will be shallow. As sleep is extremely important to your mental health, you should aim to keep alcohol to lower levels or cut it out altogether.

Alcohol affects your sleep

Ultimately, alcohol is more likely to be a coping mechanism than the source of your problems. You can try to change your drinking habits but if you are not changing your thinking you may always default back to that coping mechanism. As mentioned earlier, a ping-pong ball can easily be put back into an empty glass, but once filled with hope it is much harder for that ball to return. Simply trying to stop drinking by will power alone will seldom work. Escape mechanisms, such as drinking, need to be replaced with healthier alternatives rather than stopped, but ultimately it is your thoughts you need to change.

Guilt, shame, feelings of being unloved, failing etc., can all drive people to the bottle. Depression sufferers can sometimes feel guilty for being depressed so are easily driven to drink. Your reach for alcohol is because deep down you feel unloved, insecure and insignificant. The only way to solve your alcohol problem is to deal with these three feelings.

You may want to consider the following coping strategies:

1. *Discipline comes in the supermarket not at home:*
   There is a danger that if you buy a bottle of wine that, after the first glass, it will be difficult to stop. Therefore, buy a small, one glass capacity, bottle of wine. Try to avoid keeping alcohol in the house and only purchase what you intend to drink that evening.

2. *Don't take your card to the pub:*
   If going to the pub take cash and no card. If you only take £10 in your wallet, then you are limited to only drinking two pints. To prevent going out with your wallet, you may need to plan to go to a cash-machine earlier in the day or keep some cash at home.

3. *Buy more expensive drinks:*
   When we buy something that is beyond our normal price range we tend to eat or drink it slower. Of course, there needs to be a little wisdom in this in order not to be excessive or get into financial problems. Drinking one pint of gourmet beer at £6 a pint might seem crazy, but it will limit your intake. If the pints were £3 each you would probably drink two in possibly the same time, and, in reality, spend the same amount. If pints cost £2.50 in a bar you might drink even more in the same amount of time; say three pints at a total cost of £7.50. A higher price can actually limit our intake because we are more likely to drink slowly.

71

4. Combine strategy 2 and 3 for the best option.

Any addiction can steal hope. Drugs and alcohol may give temporary relief but in the end they are destructive. They can lead to other problems such as financial worries, broken relationships, or bursts of anger, which can later result in moments of regret. The drugs are not the main problem, it's the way you view yourself.

Ultimately, what helps set you free from alcohol problems is dealing with the source of your insecurities, feelings of insignificance and lack of acceptance. Alcohol is a coping mechanism and as you instil hope into your life there is no longer a need to use those coping mechanisms. However, if you have a serious drug or alcohol problem, you should seek professional advice or attend a rehab clinic.

Diet and Food

Diet can affect our mood so it is important to eat healthily. Sadly the soils over the years have increasingly become depleted of vitamins. Vitamin B12 and other vitamin supplements are recommended to make up for this deficiency. Caffeine, sugar and gluten have also been common factors in making us tired, which is when we can become more susceptible to negative thoughts. Caffeine can also inhibit the absorption of vitamins. There are hundreds of books and tips available on improving your diet. The best way to change your diet is to vary it until you see some alleviation of your symptoms.

There is also a tendency to become over-obsessed with changing diet. Whilst altering your diet may have an effect on depression, it may be minimal compared to altering your thought life.

Physical Contact

I'm British, so sadly physical contact is something that I'm not used too. Physical contact is important and therapeutic. Obviously, we cannot simply touch other people or force them to touch us, so we need to be careful. It can sometimes feel awkward allowing someone to touch us if we are not used to it, so you may need to face that fear.

A study was undertaken in a nursing home where residents were given pets. The residents that had a pet they could stroke and receive affection from were reported to live longer and have better states of minds. I have found that animals can provide therapeutic relief for moments of depression. Of course, you may not be able to afford a cat or dog, but that doesn't mean you need to rule it out altogether. I have walked other people's dogs and stroked other peoples cats.

Physical contact won't solve depression, and is more of a coping mechanism than a solution. Some people go too far with this coping mechanism and use sex as a way to deal with their problems, which in turn can lead to further problems and enhance depression.

Your environment

There are many people in the world who live in difficult environments but remain positive and have a great deal of hope. Some of the Holocaust survivors had a remarkably positive attitude despite their environments. Ideally, our emotions shouldn't be dictated by our environment, but sometimes it is a contributing factor. One of the things that can help our mood, is to de-clutter, tidy and clean. When we are organised and there is less clutter in view, it is easier to relax. You may have also collected a lot of clutter over the years that you don't need. Do you have lots of shoes in your closet that you never wear? Books you will never read again? Having a good clear-out can make you feel a bit more upbeat and might help you to take your mind off any ruminating thoughts. I always clear up whilst listening to music.

Not only tidying but a change of environment is useful. It can help refocus our minds; give us a new perspective of our problems and a more positive outlook on life.

Tidying your environment
helps tidy your thoughts

Changing location will change
your thoughts

What is your work environment like? Can you make any improvements? The following list of words may help you think about how you can improve your environment:

- Clutter
- Ergonomics
- Lighting
- Colours
- Airflow
- Noise

Light

Lighting can have a big effect on our mood. Too little natural sunlight can lead us to feel depressed as it is a source of vitamin D. The light we choose indoors can also affect us. Experiment with different coloured light bulbs, from warm to cool tones. Generally speaking, warmer colours will help us relax more. Dimming the lights before bedtime can be helpful to induce sleep.

As previously mentioned, excessive use of smartphones can contribute to increased tiredness, anxiety and depression. It can also lead to forms of "Obsessive Compulsive Disorder" which may increase depression. It is good to monitor how much you look at your smartphone especially in the evenings. Staring at a phone just before going to bed will reduce your ability to fall and maintain good sleep, therefore using your phone before bedtime is inadvisable. How much do you <u>need</u> to look at your phone?

When I was working in an office I had a computer that was placed in front of the window – this contrast of the computer screen and backlight led to a lot of headaches. You spend a third of your life at work – it is important to get the lighting right. A good boss will take the position of your computer into consideration.

Exercise

When I was depressed I never felt I had the energy to exercise. However, it is a important aspect of recovery. Exercise can be daunting in moments of depression, with thoughts such as "I'm too tired to exercise".

Jane feels depressed. Bob pops by to visit her.

> *Bob:* I think we should go for a walk round the park.
>
> *Jane:* No sorry Bob. I'm too tired to do exercise. I can't exercise. I'm not well enough.
>
> *Bob:* Can I have a cup of tea?
>
> *Jane:* Yes sure. I'll put the kettle on.

Jane walks to the kitchen

> *Bob:* I thought you said you couldn't exercise.

Jane: I can't.

Bob: But you just did! You walked into the kitchen. And you walked down the stairs this morning.

Jane: True

Bob: Now it's the same distance between the front door and the gate at the front drive than it is from your bedroom into the kitchen and back. In fact, it should be easier to walk to the front gate because there are no stairs. Do you think you can do that?

Bob and Jane walk to the front gate and back.

Bob: So I'm sure you can exercise - you just did.

Bob calls back the next day. He asks Jane to walk to the gate plus a few extra steps. Does she do it? Yes! The following day he walks with Jane to the house next door. When Bob arrives the conversation is as follows:

Bob: Shall we go for a walk in the park?

Jane: Oh no – I can't do that. It's too much. I don't have enough energy.

Bob: Okay so yesterday you walked from the front door to the house next door – that's 25 metres each way. Let's go to the park and walk 25 metres then turn around and walk back. If you can walk 25 metres to the next door neighbour, and you can, you did it yesterday, you can walk 25 metres in a park.

Jane: True

Bob drives Jane to the park and they walk 25 metres. They

gradually increase it over the next month by small steps.

If Jane continued to increase the length each day, she would eventually be able to walk around the whole park without being daunted. The problem with targets, and especially exercise, is that we see it as one big target. We need to break targets down into smaller steps.

In 2015 I ran in a half-marathon. When I started, the idea of 13 miles daunted me. However, I didn't focus on that target to begin with. I focused on running half-a-mile, then one mile, then gradually increased it. The problem when we are depressed is that we imagine a walk in the park as a long arduous task. Our imagination is exaggerating how difficult the task is. For example, you could go to the park and simply walk two steps, and that would still be a walk in the park. It's good to start with small steps.

Ideally, you want to be able to get up to a 30 minute workout. Aerobic exercises should continue for at least 30 minutes for them to be effective. Also, be aware not to over-exert yourself. Many people feel an emotional low after an exhausting event. If you use a lot of adrenaline, you need to be cautious that you do not spiral into depression afterwards – so be guard your thoughts much more carefully after intense exercise.

"If you can't fly then run, if you can't run then walk, if you can't walk then crawl, but whatever you do you have to keep moving forward."
Martin Luther King

**Exercise is vital.
Start with small steps.
Remember, results don't
come immediately, so persevere.**

**"Perseverance is not a long race; it is
many short races one after the other"**
Walter Elliot

Relaxation

When you relax do you truly relax? I like the phrase "It's only a game". Occasionally I play snooker. I'm not particularly good – I think my highest break has been about 18 so far (blue, pink, black). Sometimes I can end up beating myself up when not potting a shot – I am allowing perfectionism to creep into a hobby – a hobby which is supposed to be relaxing. Similarly, someone might go to the beach and think they are relaxing, but, in reality, they are spending all the time on their phone looking at emails or solving mathematical equations. Mindfulness can help us relax, whilst perfectionism will steal peace of mind. Please refer to the subsequent sections on these.

Perfectionism can creep into your hobbies and ruin the pleasure.

Relaxation is vital. Some people feel guilty when relaxing because they are not working and others feel like they are wasting time. You need time to relax, as your brain does a lot of processing during rest. It can also help you to have a fresh perspective when returning to work.

It is important to change your lifestyle, to make time for relaxation.

Summary

1. Develop healthy sleeping habits.

2. You have more energy than you realise.

3. Hope instils energy.

4. Choose your music wisely.

5. Be careful with your intake of alcohol.

6. Keep a healthy diet.

7. Physical contact can help develop acceptance.

8. Adapt your environment.

9. Consider how light is affecting you.

10. Exercise.

11. Try to maintain good general health.

12. Relax

CHANGE YOUR CIRCUMSTANCES

Your circumstances may have a huge impact on how you think and your emotional health. What are your circumstances? They can be divided into various categories:

- Work
- Vision
- Where you live
- Finances
- Family
- Friendships / Loneliness
- Partner / Singleness
- Hobbies
- Sport

In recent years there have been a lot of phrases that seem to have entered society such as:

> "If you can't change your circumstances,
> change your attitude."

> "If you can't do anything about it, then let it go.
> Don't be a prisoner to things you can't change."

Whilst there is a great deal of truth in these statements there is, however, one particular danger. In both of the above statements, there is an assumption that "we know whether we can change our circumstances". However, we are not omniscient (all-knowing) and therefore it is often difficult to know what we can truly change. Consider the following:

Mike has just bought his first car and is ignorant of the fact that his car has a spare tyre in the boot. On the way home his car breaks down. He sits there and thinks "Well, I can't change my circumstances, so I just need to let go. I need to change my attitude." But what Mike doesn't realise is that he _can_ indeed change his circumstances – he is just ignorant of what he can do.

A lot of people may use phrases, like those above, as an excuse or to admit defeat. Firstly, realise that your potential to change your circumstances is probably greater than you realise. You may need to explore more avenues, seek advice, and combat fears, but it will be worth it in the end.

Fear is a huge barrier to changing your circumstances. A lot of people may admit defeat, thinking that they can't change their circumstances when the truth is they can. It is fear that is preventing them from changing their circumstances.

**You have more potential to change
your circumstances than you realise.**

You may underestimate your ability to change.

What can you do to change your circumstances? One useful way to work out what you can do to change a circumstance is by looking at stories where others have been in a similar situation. Let's say the problem is extra dumped rubbish in your neighbourhood. Perhaps another town had a similar problem and the residents came up with a solution. Can you implement the same solution? If you can't find any stories where someone overcame the same circumstances, you might be able to be the first. You might become a pioneer! Let's say the council is not filling up the potholes in the road. You might form a group of volunteers, collect money, and then present a case to the local council where your group gain permission to fill in the holes on their behalf. Sometimes it requires thinking outside the box, using your imagination.

**Testimonies of what others have achieved
can help change your circumstances.**

**Use your imagination. Think outside the box.
Think creatively.**

**Become a pioneer!
Change your circumstances.**

Work

In the "Change your thinking" sections we deal with your attitude to work and how to improve your outlook on your work. However, if you are spending your life doing something you don't enjoy, then no matter how much you change your thought life, there will always be a danger of reverting back to negative rumination.

Firstly, let us recognise that "a perfect job" does not exist. All jobs will have their challenges and setbacks. However, if you find that the majority of your time you dread work, then it might be that you have chosen a career for the wrong motives or one that doesn't suit you.

It might be that the work you are undertaking is what you really like doing but the company is not treating you well. Rather than bottle it up it is best to air your views. Bosses may be relieved to hear your views. Companies may be willing to make changes in order to make your work life more rewarding. Remember that without airing your views there is little chance things will automatically change. Be proactive. You need to air your views in order to see change. Make suggestions for improvements rather than simply complain. It might mean that you have to take on new responsibilities or be creative with solutions.

Your work is ultimately linked to your vision in life. In order to change your circumstances you may need to change your vision.

Vision

"Where there is no vision the people perish"[12]

You may call it fate, your vision, your calling, or your reason for existing. People who have a clear vision of what they want to achieve and where they are heading will be less prone to depression. They are too busy thinking about arriving at the next train station to notice the abandoned car wrecks on the side of the railway.

Your vision needs to be realistic but also stretch you. You should make a longer-term vision but break that down into manageable smaller steps. If I have the goal of going to the shop to buy a loaf of bread, the vision doesn't give me huge amounts to look forward to and is easily realised – so hope is short-lived. If I have a vision that in five years time I want to live in a foreign country and make smaller visions to make that come true, then as I see each of those small steps realised, it fills me with hope for the longer-term vision. In addition, as you complete each small step, see it as a sign that you can do more.

**Get a long-term vision that
contains smaller steps.**

It is also important to recognise that happiness is not a destination but the ability to enjoy the steps. Your ultimate goal may be to reach the bank on the other side of the river but you should enjoy each stepping stone. If you don't reach the bank, remember it is better to aim at the sun and hit the moon than aim at nothing and hit every time. What have you achieved that you wouldn't have if you hadn't started out?

It is good to measure progress when making long-term visions; to see where you were and where you are now. Also, visions that involve doing good for other people will be more likely to instil hope. For example, if your vision is to build a homeless shelter in your community, you may have more hope and enjoyment than if it is a more selfish goal like building yourself an extension. It is important to be outward looking.

We are sometimes deceived into believing what our calling in life is. Your calling in life is probably the thing you are most happy doing, not necessarily what you are best at doing. Teachers or parents can deceive children into believing what they should be when they are older. You may be a fantastic musician at school and therefore your parents and teachers tell you that your calling in life is to be a musician; that this is your potential.

You may feel that if you abandon your talents you are not living up to your potential. The truth is that all of us have more than one potential. Jacqueline du Pré certainly lived up to her potential as a musician, but did she live up to her potential to be happy, or her potential as wife etc? In the wonderful film "Hilary and Jackie" (1998) Jacqueline asks André if he could still love her if she didn't play the cello. It's a remarkable insight into a character who suffered deeply with issues of love, acceptance, security and significance. Sad to say that this is common amongst highly talented, well-known celebrities.

I may not have lived up to my potential – this is inevitable because I have potential in many areas.

Also, you may feel that you are not living up to your potential because other people are getting in the way. Again recognise that you have more than one potential. You have the potential to have a positive mindset despite the people who frustrate you. We tend to think of the top-earning businessmen as big shots. But not all these big shots are happy. Status doesn't equal contentment. Would you rather be a "big-shot and unhappy" or a "semi-big-shot and happy"?

Success is not a destination – it is a state of mind. Your best potential is to live up to that.

I believe a lot of people have been misled into what their calling in life is. They make false assumptions such as "I can play the guitar, therefore my calling in life is to be a pop star." Realise that you may have more than one potential and what you're good at doesn't necessarily equate to what you'll be most happy doing.

Your calling is good if it is based on some key principles:

- I'm not doing this to gain approval (as a primary motivation).
- I'm not doing this to earn lots of money (as a primary motivation).
- I'm not doing this to pay the bills (as a primary motivation).
- I can look at my work and appreciate it, even if others don't.

There is also an argument that "what you are not so good at" might be your calling in life because it requires you to take more risks. For example, compare the following:

86

Jackie No.1 is *excellent at music* and *not so good at acting*. She decides to become a musician; it's easy for her, she works regular hours and never has to take risks or worry about anything. She seldom has to rely on others for advice or support because she is the best. It's smooth sailing. However, she doesn't particularly enjoy her job.

Jackie No.2 is also *excellent at music* and *not so good at acting*. She decides to become an actress. She has to pluck up the courage to dance on stage, she has to take risks and learn to trust others for advice and help in what she does. It's not easy for her and she is faced with many challenges. However, she keeps a good perspective, can see that she is improving, gets paid for what she does and enjoys the adventure.

Along comes a trauma or huge challenge; a redundancy, marriage breakup, loss of a child etc. Who is more able to cope with the situation? Jackie No.2 has developed lots of relationship skills, an ability to trust others, an ability to ask for advice. She has developed courage by taking risks and pushing herself out of her comfort zone. She is much more able to deal with the problems of life.

Now which Jackie lived up to their potential as a human being? Jackie No.1 lived up to her potential as a musician, but failed to live up to her potential to be happy, courageous and build supportive relationships. Jackie No.2 may have failed to live up to her potential as a musician but lived up to her potential to be happy, courageous and trust in relationships. Do what you feel you are called to do, and what you enjoy – not what you feel you have to do. Find your calling.

In order to find your calling, you may have to ask yourself where you want to be in five years time. Most people find this difficult to answer, and a lot of people are too scared to make goals, fearing that they won't hit them. Sometimes it is better to take risks, because it is better to aim at the sun and hit the moon than aim at nothing and hit every-time.

Where do you see yourself in five years time?

There are many who are living below their potential, because they don't know their identity and they don't know where they are heading. Building self-esteem and good mental health will help you discover your vision and direction in life.

False vision

> "We've all been raised on television to believe that one day we'd all be millionaires, and movie gods, and rock stars. But we won't. And we're slowly learning that fact. And we're very, very pissed off."
> *Fight Club*

This quote from the film Fight Club is very true. There are a lot of people who have strong ambitions to become pop stars, celebrities or multi-millionaires. Sadly some parenting and schooling have led people to believe that they can become whoever they want to become. Teachers and parents want to encourage but sometimes end up giving false praise and this can lead people to believe that they are much more talented than they really are. Sadly these people become rather deluded into believing that something is their calling in life.

> Dylon sings, plays the guitar and wants to be a global pop star. However, he cannot sing in tune and his songs are mediocre. Sadly, he doesn't know this. His teachers at school, parents and friends, didn't want to offend his feelings so actively encouraged him to keep writing songs. In an attempt to encourage him they told Dylon his songs were really good. They also bought his

album out of pity, rather than because they genuinely wanted to buy it. Dylon now believes he is an awesome musician because he has been given so much false praise. Sadly, because he views himself as an awesome musician, he stops taking music lessons or actively seeking to improve his musical ability. Ten years later, Dylon has taken no advice from others; his musical abilities haven't improved, and he still sings out of tune, mediocre songs. He struggles to understand why he isn't a rock star with thousands of fans across the globe. Dylon is actually an excellent writer but his false view of himself as a rock star has overshadowed this.

Sadly this seems the story of many. False encouragement and false praise end up instilling false hopes into children and adults, and they end up chasing a dream which was never them in the first place. They end up trying to be a second-rate Michael Jackson instead of a first-rate teacher or first-rate writer. The longer the false praise, false encouragement and false hope last, the harder it is to come to a realisation that "This is not what I was meant to do with my life – I've been chasing a red herring."

**Be a first-rate you,
not a second-rate anyone else.**

Young passions

When you are 11 years old, the constraints of life aren't generally imposed upon you. Your criteria for your dream job are not normally based on the following:

1. I must earn £30k or more
2. I must have a 4 bedroom house
3. I must own a Mercedes

4. My job must provide enough money for xyz
5. I need to become famous

When you are younger, you aren't trying to choose your career based on adult-imposed constraints. Walter Murch, an Oscar winning film editor's, reason for being an editor was to simply carry on the passions of boyhood – to make his childhood passions a career. What were you passionate about at 11? Why did you lose that passion? Was it due to adult constraints?

Write down your goals

Writing down your goals is useful because it helps you to think what you want to achieve and why. What are your goals? Your goals may be divided into various categories: character goals, achievement goals, material goals. For example:

Character goals:
- I would like to become more generous.
- I would like to be better at making conversation.
- I would like to be more patient.

Achievement goals:
- I would like to save money for a nice holiday.
- I would like to write a book.
- I would like to learn how to ski.

Material goals:
- I would like to buy a new sofa.
- I would like to buy a new bed.
- I would like to own a grand piano.

Once you've written down your goals it is good to question them because it helps to clarify them:

- Why do you want to achieve these goals?

- When do you want to achieve these goals by? Why?

- What are the *emotional* benefits and costs of these goals?

- What are the *financial* benefits and costs of these goals?

- What are the *material* benefits and costs of these goals?

- How will these goals affect your *relationships* – in terms of benefits and costs?

- How will these goals affect your *character* – in terms of benefits and costs?

- Are you trying to obtain this because others around you have told you to do so?

- Are there any other ways you can achieve these goals?

- Do you really want to achieve these goals?

It can be useful to think of alternative ways to achieve your goals. A couple of years ago I wrote down some goals. Some goals have become less important and some goals I have found alternative solutions to. Some examples are as follows:

1. Material goal "Own a grand piano": This goal has been refocused. In order to own a grand piano, I would need a lot of money and also a big room to put it in. Firstly, I can enjoy playing my upright piano more. Secondly, if I played a grand piano all the time, I might take it for granted. Thirdly, a cheaper way to play on a beautiful grand piano is to make friends with someone who already owns one!

2. Character goal "Become more generous": whilst I'm not the most generous person in the world I've learnt to be a bit more generous. I have also learnt that generosity is not defined by money. You can become more generous with your encouragement, kind comments to others, and giving time to others.

3. Achievement goal "Run a Half Marathon": now that I have run a half marathon I know I have the capacity to do it again. I know that I can muster up some energy when I need it.

Now looking at these goals I can see that I have achieved and made progress towards these goals. It is good to measure progress over the long-term, and praise short term goals when you meet them.

Where you live

Where you live can have an impact on your depression. Do you want to live there? Do you have to live there?

According to studies over the recent decades, the average distance between where you live and the rest of your family has increased substantially. Hundreds of years ago people would make friends at school for life. Most people would stay in the same town for their life and therefore would always have friends and family around. Nowadays the situation is different. After students move to university they will often stay in that town or move again to another town. Statistics suggest that the average person lives about 31 miles away from their parents with it increasing to about 47 miles for higher earners.[13]

Increased distance from your family could contribute to depression. You may find yourself more lonely or with less of a support network. Of course, this is dependent on how supportive your family is. Living near family is generally good. Only in some rare instances distancing yourself from relatives such as abusive ones may be a healthier option. Also, be aware that if you are depressed, you may assume that your family are less supportive than they really are.

After I had a serious bout of depression, I moved back to my home town where my family live. My father, mother and brothers are supportive. They took some daily burdens off my shoulders and allowed me to focus on developing good mental health. Some things like simply washing clothes felt like an enormous effort, so the little things they did for me really helped.

Commuting can be stressful, alternatively it can help to separate your work from the rest of your life. I once had a two minute walk to work. In contrast, I've had to travel over an hour to get to work. On some commutes the roads have been quiet, and on others I have faced heavy traffic.

Traffic jams can be particularly stressful. Is there any way you can avoid that stress? Perhaps you can take an alternative route, or use another mode of transport such as the train.

Where you live might also have an impact on your social life. If you are interested in board games, a place like London will have lots of interesting events and socials where you can meet like-minded people. However, if you are into hill walking, living in London might not be the best option. The following questions are all worth considering.

- Why do you live where you live?
- What are your priorities?
- What can your wallet afford?
- Would it be better to live further away from work in a place you like and commute?

- Would you be better off living closer to work?
- Where would the best place for your social life be?
- Are your family supportive? Can you live closer to them?
- Can you move closer to a best friend?
- Do you like it here?
- Is traffic, noise or air pollution affecting your life?

It is interesting to note that statistics suggest that you are more likely to suffer with depression living in a large city, such as London, than in a town. Some reasons for this are:

- You are more likely to have financial worries
- There is more noise pollution
- There is more air pollution
- People can feel lonelier in cities
- There is more potential to envy and compare yourself in a city
- People have less time for relaxation

Whilst I do not believe that where you live is the primary reason for being depressed, it can be a contributing factor. Living in an area where you have the maximum support, healthy social life and least stress can be important to your mental well-being.

Finances

Our finances are part of our circumstances. In theory, our finances shouldn't determine our mood; we know this is possible because there are poor people who are happy and rich people who are sad. However, the reality for most of us is that finances do have an impact on our mood. For those with little disposable income, worry is often a big factor. For those with lots of money spending can be used as a coping mechanism – but in the long-term fails to satisfy.

Jessica had an excellent job as a teacher. She found her job stressful and, for reasons unknown to her, had fallen into depression. At the weekends she would go out and spend money to fill in the void – her lack of hope for the future. Despite returning 60% of what she bought she had already accumulated debts exceeding £20,000 on her credit cards.

A couple of weeks later Jessica was signed off work with depression. Now Jessica had all the time in the world and felt more lonely and depressed. Her coping mechanism was to go out shopping – retail therapy. As a result, she ended up purchasing more on her credit card and ended up in a cycle of shopping and then feeling guilty for being in debt.

Spending money can become a coping mechanism. In Jessica's instance her shopping habits were contributing to her depression. If you are depressed, and in debt, and go out and spend more money on your credit card, it can end up being a vicious cycle. Shopping therapy does not ultimately help your mental health, it can make things worse.

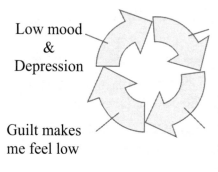

Low mood & Depression

Guilt makes me feel low

Spending money used as a coping mechanism

I now have bigger debts. I feel guilty for spending money and guilty for being more in debt.

Some people, when they feel depressed, will end up being so harsh on themselves that they need to practise a little more kindness.

> Gustav is also a teacher. He earns a good salary and he has a lot of savings. Gustav is not married and he doesn't have a mortgage. He is signed off work with depression. A couple of weeks later he needs to go to town. It's two miles walk to town. A return bus ticket is £3.80. He would feel guilty if he bought a ticket to town, he should be saving money for a rainy day. Gustav never spends money, he feels guilty for doing so.

It's possible to be so harsh on yourself that you end up getting depressed for spending money – for buying a coffee at £2.75 when you could have had one down the road in another coffee shop for £2.65, or even had one at home considerably cheaper. I'm not endorsing going out and spending all your money – but you shouldn't feel guilty for being kind to yourself.

Are you saving money for a rainy day?
Perhaps it is raining today!

Dealing with finances can be tricky when you suffer with depression especially if your work pay has been cut or you find yourself out of work. Some things to consider are as follows:

- Always pay your bills on time
- Switch your bills and credit cards to direct debit so that you don't need to worry about paying them.
- Don't feel forced into buying rounds in pubs. It can be expensive – put your foot down.
- Ask relatives or friends for advice or help

Family

Your family are a part of your circumstances, however, you cannot change your family. Your father and mother, brothers and sisters will always be a part of your family. As mentioned in the "Where you live" section, living nearer to your family may be advisable for people who suffer with depression and have a supportive family. It's much harder to change your family circumstances than your job, or where you live, or your friends; in some cases it may be impossible. For instance, if you have an alcoholic mother it would be difficult to change her. You have a certain degree of control over your job, but little, if any, control over the actions of others. Therefore, the phrase "If you can't change your circumstances change your attitude" rings extra loud when it comes to family issues.

Friendships

Unlike your family circumstances you have much more control over who you socialise with; your friends or lack of them. You can walk away from friends and you can make new ones.

Do not be deceived, bad company corrupts character. The company you choose will also be vital to your mental state – are your friends reinforcing the negative thoughts you are having? In that case, you may have to find new friends or talk to them about what they are saying.

Janet worries a lot about the economy and losing her job. She meets with her friends. That evening they all talk about the economy, how it is declining and how uncertain the future will be. Each friend believes they are getting "their worries off their chest" but, in reality, it has turned into group-worrying or group-rumination. In reality, her friends are making her worries worse.

One suggestion for Janet would be to walk away and find new friends. However, there is a danger that if she walks away from everyone who is negative she will eventually end up alienating the whole world.

If you distance yourself from everyone who hurts you, you'll eventually isolate yourself from the world.

Friends can vary their conversation. I have found that certain friends can be extremely positive when doing a particular activity with them, such as playing squash, but then extremely negative when doing another activity, such as going for a drink at the pub. In such instances, it might be worth limiting yourself to the friendship only when they are at their best so that you benefit from their positive friendship but not dragged down by their negative friendship.

Once people are aware of what is happening they may be less likely to do it. Friends might be much more agreeable and willing to change than you realise. If friends are making you feel emotionally drained by group-rumination then it is worth trying to:

1. Tell your friends that you don't like group-worrying or group-rumination. And that by talking about certain topics they are making things worse.

2. Try changing the topics of conversation away from those which worry you.

Nonetheless, if your friends are constantly emotionally wearing you down, you may need to walk away or create some healthy boundaries. Your friendships can have a considerable effect on your mental health, so it is worth considering whether you can change your friendship circumstances.

"Contrary to popular belief, I do not believe that friends are necessarily the people you like best; they are merely the people who got there first" *Sir Peter Ustinov*

Loneliness

Loneliness can hugely contribute to depression. Loneliness can be divided into various categories:

Physical Loneliness

Physical loneliness can exist if you are not surrounded by enough people. If someone is stranded on a desert island, they will most likely suffer this kind of loneliness. We are designed to be around people, to experience touch and communication. I am currently writing this in a library. I am not talking to anyone but the sense of people being around me makes me feel more connected than if I were at home on my own. Part of this is because I feel like I'm sharing the same space. Sharing in life is important.

Mental Loneliness

Mental loneliness is more a feeling of disconnect with the environment around you. The expression "lonely in a crowd" springs to mind. You may be sharing space, experiencing touch, and communicating with people but still feel as though you are on your own. This is mental loneliness and is more about your understanding of acceptance.

Spiritual Loneliness

The word "Spiritual" is a difficult word to define. There are some people who define spiritual as a divine connection; there are others who would define spiritual as a connection to the universe; and there are people who define themselves as spiritual atheists. Depending on your world view, this type of loneliness may or may not be one you believe in.

Romantic Loneliness

This could potentially be a sub-category of physical, mental and spiritual loneliness. As humans we crave touch, and most of us desire to be in a romantic relationship.

False Loneliness

Sometimes we perceive loneliness incorrectly. People will say they feel lonely on a Sunday afternoon, when in fact they are actually bored or don't know what to do. I remember a particular Sunday afternoon when the weather was hot. A lot of my interests are indoors; playing the piano, using the computer; cooking etc. I didn't want to be indoors on such a beautiful day, and I'd spent the morning reading and mowing the lawn. So what was I going to do next? For a fleeting moment I thought "I'm lonely", but then I realised that it wasn't loneliness – it was just that I'd drawn a blank about what to do next. I stopped and considered what to do next and came up with the idea of studying the local history of the town by doing a self-guided walk. I guess there are two ways to look at this – I was genuinely lonely but suppressed my loneliness by finding something interesting to do. Or secondly, misinterpret indecision, or boredom, as loneliness.

It is important to make the distinction between these different types of loneliness. If you don't, you may go about solving loneliness in the wrong way. For example,

Ryan feels lonely, so he decides to join lots of sports groups and go to lots of parties. He still feels lonely. He gives up. His thoughts are as follows: "I feel lonely. I joined lots of sports groups and still feel lonely. I shouldn't do. There is something wrong with me." Ryan was suffering from "mental loneliness" and tried to solve it using a solution for "physical loneliness" - it backfired.

Laura feels lonely, she decides to sign up to a dating agency.

She has a few dates with people online, and starts a relationship with Harry. She still feels lonely – she can't understand why. Laura spends most of the day at home on her own. Laura works in an office and her work is actually easy. She completes it quickly and has long periods of boredom. She thought her loneliness was because she didn't have a partner, however, in reality, she was suffering more from boredom.

Dealing with loneliness

Firstly, it is important to recognise the relationships you already have in your life. Loneliness is being "relationship poor", and like being "financially poor", it is relative. Someone in the UK may complain of being financially poor, but if they had to spend a month living in Burundi, they would most likely change their perspective. We may complain of loneliness, but if we were locked up as a hostage, or had to sail single-handedly round the globe, we might realise how blessed we actually are. However, just because there is someone lonelier than you, it doesn't mean your pain is insignificant. But be aware that a lot of people are suffering with loneliness.

You are not alone in your loneliness.

Secondly, community is good for us. If you are suffering from depression, physical loneliness will only contribute to it. Loneliness is particularly difficult as it gives us a lot of time to "ruminate" on negative thoughts. It's more difficult to think the same thoughts when you are in the company of others. To a large extent, other people define what you think about. If someone starts talking about beaches and sand, you start thinking about those things. Other people can help pull you away from your own negative thinking. This is one of the reasons that community is good, it forces us to stop ruminating.

Community is good for us.

**Isolating yourself will only
make things worse.**

In order to find friends, you may need to experiment going to
new places and meeting new people. This can be daunting for
some and so overcoming your fears and worries will be key.

- What kind of friends do you want to have?

- Where will you find those people?

The great thing is there are lots of lonely people wanting a
friend. You are not alone in your loneliness. So the best way to
find friends is to be a friend to someone else.

**If you haven't many friends,
be a friend to someone else.**

The following ideas may be useful in finding new friends:

1. Take up a new hobby e.g. join a creative writing group, football club.

2. Get involved with volunteering.

3. Volunteer to be an extra on a film, amateur productions are always looking.

4. Join a choir (this is highly recommended for alleviating depression symptoms).

5. Join a church (churches often have a good sense of community).

6. Start taking lessons e.g. swimming or piano lessons. It may be only the professional company of one, but that is better than nothing.

7. Hang out in coffee shops. Sometimes it is better to simply have people around to distract you from your thoughts. You might get to know the regulars.

8. Hang out at the sauna. It is a great place to have a light informal chat.

9. Meetup.com: This is a wonderful way to meet new people.

Partner / Singleness

Having a partner or leaving your partner is not the answer to all your life's problems. People who are married still struggle with loneliness, sexual frustration, fears etc. Being single or dealing with a difficult relationship is more of a thinking issue than circumstantial. However, in some circumstances, it may be necessary to leave an abusive or difficult relationship. Only do this with considerable forethought.

Single people who suffer from loneliness may think that by having a partner they will be less depressed. If you are unhappy, expecting the opposite sex to make you happy can be futile. As Susan Jeffers writes: 'I was still expecting the men in my life to "make me happy"'[14] and "The man in your life could stand on his head for you, as some of them in my life tried to do, but it is never enough". Susan believed her unhappiness and loneliness stemmed from what we referred to in the previous section as "romantic loneliness" – in reality it wasn't this kind of loneliness. People believe that being married or in a relationship will solve all kinds of problems; their insecurities, loneliness, sexual frustrations, financial issues etc. It often doesn't solve these, and will, in some cases, create more issues. You should look for direct solutions for these issues. If you are looking for someone to make you happy that may only backfire. Besides, there are thousands of happy single people. Rather than put all your eggs in one basket it may be better to develop lots of healthy friendships than one intimate relationship. It's *probably* better to have 12 good friends and no partner than have a partner and zero friends.

Having said this, many of us would like a partner. If you are single, changing your circumstances may be rather tricky, as it is impossible to force anyone to be your partner. However, you can put yourself in places and situations where you are more likely to meet someone.

It's better to be single than in a relationship that isn't working out.

The grass is always greener on the other side of the fence.

Are you trying to find your own identity in another human? Who would you be without a partner?

Hobbies and Sport

Your hobbies, including your sports, are circumstances. Your hobbies can contribute to depression in as much as you may be doing hobbies you no longer enjoy. Sometimes we take up hobbies or sports because of friends. Is it a hobby you *really* enjoy? What drives you and what thoughts do you have as a result of those hobbies?

George took up gymnastics because he liked one of the girls in the class. After a while, the girl left but George didn't and still doesn't enjoy gymnastics. He goes out of routine and also in the hope he'll meet another girl. His thoughts are often focused on how he failed with the girl and how he isn't as good as the other gymnasts. George clearly is doing a hobby out of duty, because he's always done it, and for alternate motives - he may not realise that after a while a hobby is no longer enjoyable. Why doesn't he do something else where he is more likely to enjoy it?

I had a similar experience with dance classes. I had been enjoying classes and the dance teacher was good. Unfortunately, she left and was replaced by a teacher who wasn't as good. After a while, it suddenly dawned on me that the lessons were not exactly enjoyable, and I was going out of habit.

Taking up new hobbies can be a way of instilling hope. Make sure that you are enjoying your hobbies and don't beat yourself up when you fail to meet your own expectations. If, for example, you are playing snooker, you should not be beating yourself up every time you miss a shot - after all this is a hobby and supposed to be fun.

Creative hobbies are particularly useful at instilling hope. Creativity is about building imaginative skills. As we do so, we also strengthen our ability to hope.

In London there is a project called Cafe Art which gives out free cameras to the homeless and then collects them a little later. The difference it makes is remarkable. It gives them a focus and hope for the future.[15]

**Creativity is great for cultivating hope;
it is the soil in which hope grows.**

Oppression not Depression

Oppression is defined as: "the exercise of authority or power in a burdensome, cruel, or unjust manner."[16]

Occasionally relatives of someone who is depressed may actually prevent a depressed person from becoming better. This normally happens on a subconscious level. For example, a husband's wife suffers with depression. Her vulnerability allows him to manipulate her through guilt and shame. If she was happy, he wouldn't feel as powerful or in control. He subconsciously wants her to remain emotionally low so he can manipulate her.

Sometimes it is difficult to recognise oppression if we are subjected to it. In an oppressed state you may be bullied into not telling someone about your problems. Strong feelings of shame often stem from oppression. For example, sexual abuse victims may have thoughts such as the following:

- "I'm dirty"
- "Nobody will understand me if I tell anyone"
- "If I tell anyone, he or she will beat me up."

If you are keeping a lot of _dark_ secrets to yourself, this _could be_ a sign of oppression. Keeping a dark secret is often toxic so you should aim to talk to someone about any traumas or negative experiences you've encountered.

If you do indeed believe you are experiencing oppression, then remember that we may have little influence or ability to change the people around us, and especially on our own. You can always tell a trusted friend if you think you are being mistreated by anyone around you. Alternatively, approach a counsellor who can deal more with the specific issue at hand.

Oppression can be subtle at times. It may be indeliberately imposed upon you, stemming from the insecurities of others. Often oppression can come from parents or people in authority such as a boss, a religious leader or teacher. Oppression can even happen despite people's best interests. Remember, we are not passing blame here. Blame looks at the past and is a waste of energy. Rather than blaming we need to simply accept that we cannot change the past and take responsibility for the future. Susan Jeffers gives a good example of subtle oppression:

> 'I once told my mother she obviously had no confidence in me, because she was worried about me all the time. She said that was ridiculous; she thought I was the smartest, most competent woman she knew. I pointed out that if this was the case, her worry was unjustified. She looked surprised, and for the first time realised that the way she habitually spoke to me was a carry-over from when I was two, and was not based on today's reality. From this conversation a miracle happened: She became one of my biggest confidence builders. "You can do it. You can do anything you set your mind to do!" Yes, that's really the way she began speaking to me.'[17]

To judge whether you are suffering from oppression as opposed to depression can be difficult. If, for example, a husband is always telling his wife that she isn't worth anything, swearing at her, calling her foul names, constantly using expletives, and manipulating his wife through fear, threat guilt and shame, this could be considered as an oppressive relationship. Manipulation by fear would often manifest itself in conditional threats such as "If you don't cook my dinner, I won't give you any money". Oppressive relationships are often found between partners; parents and children; a boss and workers; or a teacher and pupil. Obviously, if physical abuse is involved, it is almost certainly oppression.

If you believe you are in an oppressive relationship, it doesn't necessarily mean it can't be fixed. In the case of a marriage, marriage counselling can work. Also, the other person, or persons, can change. Communication is key. If you find your boss oppressive, can you be open with him/her about how they are oppressing you? For example, talk to him/her about their high demands etc.

Please also note that we need to be cautious we don't put all the blame on the other person. Blame isn't constructive. Besides, in most circumstances people who suffer in an oppressive relationship also experience depression. So it is important to deal with both issues. If any of the above resonates strongly with you, the best advice I can recommend is to find a third party who can assess your relationship. If no third party is available, then you may benefit from discussing issues with a therapist. In a situation where the oppression doesn't cease, you may want to remove or distance yourself from the other person (if possible).

Summary

1. You probably have more potential to change your circumstances than you realise.

2. Remind yourself how you have previously changed your circumstances.

3. Read stories of how other people changed their circumstances.

4. If you don't like your job it might be time for a change.

5. It is important to have vision in life.

6. Your potential is not necessarily what your teacher or other people tell you.

7. You have more than one potential.

8. Don't follow empty visions.

9. What you were passionate about at eleven years old may be a good indicator of what you are truly passionate about. Adult constraints sometimes get in the way.

10. Write down your goals and assess them.

11. Why do you live where you live?

12. Be careful how you deal with finances when you suffer with depression.

13. You can find new friends if need be.

14. You are not alone in your loneliness. It is possible to find new friends.

15. Don't put all your hopes into finding a partner if you are single.

16. If a marriage is problematic, consider marriage counselling, or, in severe circumstances, leaving.

17. Take up hobbies you are interested in.

18. Creativity is great for cultivating hope.

CHANGE YOUR THINKING - PART 2

TRUTH, MEMORY AND LIES

The way you think will often determine how depressed you are. Thoughts are one of the main contributing factors to depression. These thoughts can be categorised into a variety of topics. We will deal with each of them in turn.

Imagination

Hope is about imagining good things happening to us and others in the future. Our imagination is key to finding hope. Memory and imagination are both activated in part of the brain called the hippocampus. Imagination is created by projecting our memories onto the future. Hope is based on having a positive imagination whilst fear is based on having a negative imagination.

Sometimes I wake up to noises in the night and fear burglars coming into the house. In my imagination I see them in the house. Likewise, fears of failure, rejection, and not being able to cope are all based on how we use our imagination.

Our imaginations can limit what we do. Firstly, our fearful imaginations will prevent us from doing something. For example, if you imagine there are bombs planted all over London, your imagination may stop you from going there, regardless of whether it is true. Secondly, you are unlikely to do something you can't imagine. If you can't imagine yourself successfully skydiving, you are unlikely to do it. It took Thomas Edison some effort of imagination in order to design the light bulb. For him hope kept him going, despite his many failed attempts.

It has been said that we think in pictures. When I say the word "Butterfly", you don't think of the letters "B-U-T-T-E-R-F-L-Y" you picture a butterfly in your mind. If I say "Small red butterfly", your imagination changes; you visualise a more specific butterfly in your head. The only way you can do this is based on your memory; you've already seen a butterfly. If I then said "Red and yellow, striped butterfly" you can picture it in your head – even if you've never seen one. What you are doing here is combining memories. You imagine a new butterfly by combining: a memory of a butterfly, with your memory of red, with your memory of yellow, and your memory of stripes. This is how your imagination works. Now with your imagination you can put that butterfly on top of a blue coloured sandwich. The only way you can picture a sandwich is because you have one stored in your memory.

Your imagination is primarily based upon your memory and using new combinations of memories to create new ideas. Hope is a positive imagination of the future. Just like your memory and imagination, hope is mainly visual.

Choose a friend. In your memory picture the friend. Now in your memory picture a desert. Now remember a time when you were thirsty. Now combine all these images. You have a thirsty friend in a desert. Now picture a bottle of water on a horizon. Now imagine your friend running towards the bottle and picking it up and drinking it. Your imagination just painted hope for your friend, you saw them finding a bottle of water. It might seem an unrealistic scenario, but we can also use this for reality.

How do we develop a positive imagination in such a negative world? Along with creativity, our memory is key to developing a positive imagination. Most of the way we view the future is by projecting our memories of the past forward onto the future.

The thoughts you just had about your friend, where did they come from? The imagination you just had came from four sources:

1. Memory Knowledge (e.g. your memory of what a desert looks like)
2. Memory Stimulant (e.g. my words "desert")
3. Memory Recall – Your choice and accuracy of memory (e.g. you choose a flat desert)
4. Memory Combining – Your ability to combine memories (e.g. friend + desert)

Memory Knowledge

Firstly, your memory is linked to your knowledge. You know what a desert is and therefore you can remember it. If I told you to picture a Coles 4038, you would have difficulty picturing that because you probably don't know what it is. If it isn't in your memory you won't be able to recall it. A Coles 4038 is a type of microphone. Also, note that if your knowledge is incorrect, your ability to visualise and imagine the situation will be impaired. When I said the word "horizon", if you believed that a horizon was a star in the sky then you would have no hope for your friend reaching the bottle on top of the star. Your knowledge can be anything from your understanding of something to a view about yourself. If the knowledge is missing or incorrect it could steal your hope.

Memory Stimulant

Secondly, memories don't often randomly stream into our heads; they normally are stimulated. My words stimulated you to have the initial thoughts. I wrote the word "Desert" and therefore I am stimulating what you think about.

To a large extent, your imagination was based on what I told you to think about. In that way, we can paint pictures on other peoples minds. People have the ability to affect one another's imaginations. Other people can paint negative pictures on your mind and steal your hope, or paint positive pictures and give you hope. Therefore, it is important to feed your imagination with positive things.

Memories are mainly triggered by information that comes in through our senses: tastes, smells, sounds, music, words, touch, textures, posture, sights, location and climate. When information triggers memories, associated emotions may arise; these emotions in themselves may trigger further memories and emotions.

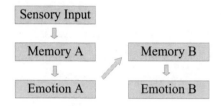

Memory Recall

The third important criteria for imagination is memory recall. Your memory is unique and therefore the type of desert you thought about was based on all the different pictures you've seen of a desert. When I said "desert" you had a choice as to what kind of desert you pictured. You may have pictured one with tall sand-dunes or a flat desert. What you choose from your memory bank will have a considerable difference to your imagination.

Even if the knowledge you were taught was correct – i.e. a desert is a dry arid place – the way your memory recalls this information is important. Sometimes when we recall our memories they can be incorrect or skewed. This is because details are forgotten and therefore we fill in these details with other knowledge we have; often making assumptions.

Memory Combining

Once you recall several memories you combine them into a new situation. You can superimpose a union jack on the wings of a butterfly etc.

So hope comes from true knowledge, stimulation, accurate recall and combining of memories. If any of these areas is incorrect, damaged or missing, you lack hope.

**HOPE = TRUTH + STIMULATION +
MEMORY CHOICE/RECALL +
MEMORY COMBINATION**

If hope comes from our imagination, and imagination is based on our memories, it is important to look at what role the memory has in recovering from depression.

Memory

The Cambridge dictionary defines depression as a "lack of hope". The hippocampus is the part of the brain that we use to hope. Interestingly the same part of the brain is used for memory. What we choose to remember is key to how we see the future. For example, consider the following scenario.

In my life I've baked 100 cakes and 60 of them came out fine and 40 I managed to burn. You ask me to bake a cake. Now if I remember the 40 I burnt and forget the 60 that came out fine, then I'll have no hope. I will probably refuse to bake, telling you that I am no good. If, however, I remember the 60 cakes I baked well and forget the 40 I burnt, I will tell you that I can bake a cake and I will be full of hope.

**Hope comes from projecting positive
memories onto the future.**

We project our memories onto the future. If what we remember is positive then we have hope, if what we remember is negative then we will be full of despair. Depression is, to a large extent, a memory problem. Recently, I found out that up to 40 percent of people with Alzheimer's disease suffer from significant depression. As I believe that depression is a memory problem this statistic comes to me as no surprise. Let's look at the scenario again with Alzheimer's.

> In my life I've baked 100 cakes and 60 of them came out fine and 40 I managed to burn. Now if you ask me to bake a cake, and if I have Alzheimer's and can't remember the 40 I burnt or the 60 that came out fine, then I'll probably think – I've never done this before and won't have any hope, and therefore probably refuse to bake you a cake.

In recovery from depression I have learnt that building a positive memory is key. The act of remembering is not passive. In the body skeletal muscles always come in pairs – these pairs can be flexed in opposite directions. Your memory is like two muscles – either they can be flexed in a positive direction or they can be flexed in a negative direction. As we practise using a positive memory, our reflexes of that side become much quicker. When we practise negativity, it strengthens the other side.

What we feed our minds with determines what we remember. What we choose to actively mull over, or meditate on, will be engraved on our memories. Returning to the analogy of baking a cake. What determines whether I remember the 40 burnt cakes or 60 good cakes? Do you think it is totally arbitrary? No; just like the flexing of the muscle, what I've practised will become the reflex action.

If I get up every morning and have a reminder on the mirror that I've baked 60 good cakes, read it every morning and meditate (mull over) on this, then when you ask me to bake a cake the memory is going to reflex in that direction. I'm more likely to remember the 60 good cakes than the 40 burnt cakes.

If you constantly read news about aeroplane crashes and then get on a plane, when there is a sudden pocket of air turbulence your memory is suddenly going to recall all the plane crashes and you will imagine a fearful image of a plane crashing. You will most likely be full of anxiety and with little hope for the future.

What are you focusing on?

Of course, memory relies on knowing the truth to start with. In an earlier chapter we discussed that will power is not the answer – that knowing the truth is.

Let's remind ourselves of the story of Bob:

> Bob works in a shop. He believes that 2+2=5. His boss keeps asking him to count the money in the till at the end of the day but Bob keeps making a mistake. Bob has now been threatened by his boss that he will lose his job if he continues to make mistakes. Bob asks his friends for advice. Some friends tell him to stop worrying about losing his job. Some of his friends tell him to believe he can do it; that if he makes a mistake it isn't the end of the world. When Bob goes back to work he miscounts the money in the till and loses his job.

If Bob has spent most of his life learning that 2+2=5, then his muscle is going to be flexed in the incorrect direction. Once he knows the truth he needs to actively remember it until 2+2=4 is an automatic reflex.

Hope is knowing the truth and then actively remembering it until it becomes an automatic reflex.

In order to actively remember things we may need to adopt strategies. Strategies are used every day by people to remember things. Some people write shopping lists to help them remember what they need to buy at the supermarket. The strategies mentioned on page 51 may help you build positive memories.

Have you noticed that life is full of recurring problems? Not every challenge in life is brand new. You text someone but they fail to reply. How often have you experienced that issue? It may be frustrating but it is often worth asking:

**Have I been in this situation before ...
if so what was the outcome?**

You will probably find that you have been in a similar situation. You may remember that during a past event you worried obsessively about an outcome, but then later on, found the outcome wasn't as bad as you thought. If you've been in a similar situation and overcome the problem, you can use your memory to instil more hope for your current problem.

In contrast, a lot of problems in life can also be new ones. Your reply to the earlier cake analogy may have been "But what if I've never baked a cake or I've burnt 100 % of cakes?"

This is where the memory of others and history can play an important part in instilling hope.

**If he can do it, so can I.
Success breeds success.**

117

Of course, some wisdom needs to be applied here, but we certainly can use the inspiration and stories of how others have overcome the odds in order to boost our levels of hope. How many people have been in debt and managed to come out of it? Thousands. So it is possible? Yes. How did they do it? What inspired them? What strategies did they use? A typical reply may be:

> "Oh but my debts are different, my debt and my situation is much worse than all those people who succeeded in getting free of it."

Really?! I think if you start observing what people have overcome, you might be rather surprised. The stories of how our ancestors overcame difficulties in past and countless films can be inspirational for us in finding ways to overcome our problems and live our dreams. You can use memory and history to evaluate the outcome of a particular challenge.

Has anyone else been in this situation – how did they resolve it?

Of course, getting out of debt, overcoming job problems, finding a new career, may be instances where you can use the phrase "If he can do it, so can I". What if you've baked 100 cakes burnt them all, decide that "If he can do it, so can I", then bake a further 50 cakes and burn all of those? At this point, I suggest considering the following points:

Get Advice – Knowledge problem

Returning to the cake analogy, thousands of people bake cakes successfully, so if you were constantly failing with baking, it may be simply an issue with not having enough advice. How many people have already done something similar to what you are achieving? If it is a lot of people, then this is almost certainly the case. You may need a teacher to help you improve your ability. You may need to swallow some pride and admit you need someone else's help. If we continue to fail it can steal our hope, so getting advice is a way to instil hope. For example, it might be that you are using the wrong type of sugar – granulated sugar instead of caster sugar. This is effectively a knowledge problem. Once you know the missing knowledge you can have hope for baking a cake once again.

Seek advice for the things you find difficult.

Remind yourself – Memory problem

It might be that you have simply forgotten the knowledge which allows you do something. If I attempted to bake a cake after many years of not practising, I might have forgotten that I'm supposed to beat the flour in gently. This, in turn, could lead to problems. In order to have hope to bake the cake I may need to refresh my knowledge. This might mean going back to the recipe, asking someone for confirmation – etc. Various things can stimulate your memory, including others.

We need to remind ourselves to find hope.

Patience – Try different not harder

Thomas Edison took over 1000 attempts to invent the light bulb. Do you think he did the same experiment each time? Most likely not. He varied his attempts. If you are not succeeding baking a cake, perhaps the recipe is not particularly good – try following a different recipe.

Try different, not harder.

Einstein said that the definition of insanity was doing the same thing over and over again expecting different results. The phrase "If you don't succeed try again" is actually slightly incorrect. It should read "If you don't succeed try another recipe". If you feel like you are going round in circles,

119

perhaps you need to vary your attempts. To instil hope, try doing something differently. Be patient as you explore different solutions to your problems.

If you don't succeed, try another recipe.

As mentioned before, in order to have hope we combine our memories in our imagination. If you imagine opening a blue door with a green key and then act on your imagination and it doesn't work, it may be that you have simply imagined the wrong combination. If you then readjust your imagination to imagine the blue key opening the blue door, you may then find the solution. I'm sure Thomas Edison imagined a variety of ways to invent the light bulb and tried them until he succeeded. Also, note that you have to act on your imagination.

Patience is key to finding success. A lot of the people we look up to, and consider successful, did not get there overnight. There are some privileged few, but they are in the minority and their fast track to success can derail them later on. Our characters need to grow at the same speed as our talents. If you became a pop star or a world-renowned footballer overnight, the chances are you might not have learnt responsibility skills, discipline skills, or vital character skills to cope with the pressures of that kind of lifestyle. What's more, being in these so-called "successful positions" is often less rewarding than you may think; a host of new problems comes with fame and success. Success really should be measured by your character.

**Success should be measured by
character not status**

Be patient with yourself

Patience is not always easy in a world where we are so used to having things instantly. Instant coffee, films on demand 24/7, and instant messaging all mislead us into the idea that this is normal. In nature "instant" isn't so common, storms take a while to build, trees take a long time to grow and eggs take a while to hatch.

Things will turn out alright in the end. If it is not alright, it is simply because you haven't reached the end.[18]

One of the biggest dangers of impatience is that we forget to enjoy the journey. Have you ever been on a journey somewhere and been impatient to arrive at your destination, then on arriving at your destination find out it wasn't all you'd expected? It might have been that the view out the car window was nicer than the place you visited. Furthermore, if it is a two hour journey to a place that you visit for only fifty minutes, you will spend more time journeying than being at the destination. Therefore, it is really important that you enjoy the journey.

Enjoy the stepping stones not the destination.

It's simply not you

Another reason we may find something doesn't bring joy or hope, is that it simply isn't fit for us. You may have dreams and challenges, but how many people can do what you are trying to achieve? If the answer is thousands, then the problem does not lie with your potential ability – it will most likely be as a result of the previous points: getting advice, patience, trying things differently or the use of your memory. If the answer is that only 1 or 2 people have achieved what you are aiming to do, such as sailing a yacht around the world single-handed, it may simply be that it is not meant to be.

You may be aiming to be a second-rate yacht racer when you could become a first-rate artist. You may feel that you are not living up to your potential, but it might be that you are heading in the wrong direction in the first place. Your lack of success is a warning signal to point you in a better, more successful direction. In this case, it is worth reading the section on vision (p.84)

HOPE = TRUTH + STIMULATION + MEMORY CHOICE/RECALL + MEMORY COMBINATION

Returning to our equation - if any part of the equation is broken it diminishes hope. Let's look at some examples of some people when they are asked to bake a cake.

Oliver can bake, however he believes that he hasn't got a cake tin in the cupboard, actually his mum put one there but he doesn't know that. He refuses to bake a cake replying "I can't, I haven't got a cake tin, and if you want this by tomorrow the shops are already closed." His lack of hope is based on the fact that he believes he doesn't have the equipment to perform the task. But indeed Oliver does have a cake tin. Oliver's problem is that he is missing some information, his knowledge is deficient, and consequently his hope is stolen.

Hope = ~~Truth~~ (Knowledge is missing) + Stimulation + Memory Choice/Recall + Memory Combination

Sophia believes that she doesn't have the ability to bake a cake. She believes she cannot follow instructions. But she is an extremely capable person, good at doing new things, and following instructions. She refuses to bake a cake replying "I can't, I'm not capable enough." Her lack of hope is based on the fact that she believes she is not capable. Sophia's problem is not one of missing knowledge but of incorrect knowledge about her own ability. Therefore, her hope is stolen.

Hope = ~~Truth~~ (Knowledge is incorrect) + Stimulation + Memory Choice/Recall + Memory Combination

Harry can bake, but he hasn't for many years. If someone reminded him about the time when he baked lots of cakes for a party, and people loved them, he would find hope to bake a cake. But his memory has not been stimulated – therefore his hope is deficient.

Hope = Truth + ~~Stimulation~~ (Stimulation is missing) + Memory Choice/Recall + Memory Combination

Alfie has baked 100 cakes, burnt 40 with 60 successful attempts. When he asked to bake a cake he remembers the 40 he already burnt. His memory choice/recall was poor and therefore his hope was stolen.

Hope = Truth + Stimulation + ~~Memory Choice/Recall~~ (Poor choice of memory) + Memory Combination

Freya has baked 100 cakes, burnt 2 with 98 successful attempts. However, when asked to bake a cake there are more factors involved. Her *friend* asked her to bake a cake. At the time her friend was also talking about holding a party for 100 guests. Freya knows she can bake a cake, but wrongly assumes that her friend is asking her to bake a cake for 100 people. In fact, her friend is only asking her to bake a small cake; her friend has also asked other people to bake cakes. By combining her memory of baking a cake and picturing a room full of 100 people, Freya's imagination has now led to a daunting prospect, an inaccurate imagination that she must bake a cake for 100 people. It's too daunting, so she loses hope, but this is based on combining two statements incorrectly.

Hope = Truth + Stimulation + Memory Choice/Recall + ~~Memory Combination~~ (The two statements were incorrectly combined)

Knowing the correct information is key to gaining hope. Truth can give us hope, but deceptive thoughts can steal our hope.

Deceptive thoughts

A common cause of depression is believing thoughts that are simply not true or may be far from the truth. These steal hope. Coming back to our cake example, if you simply believe that you are incapable of baking a cake when you actually are, this will steal your hope.

The problem with false thoughts is they happen on various levels and these errors in thinking are not always obvious. Our first combat method is to:

1. Identify negative thoughts.
2. Recognise their common characteristics.
3. Understand the way in which lies can masquerade as truths.

If a train ticket officer just lets everyone board without checking tickets, they'll soon find the carriages are full of passengers who haven't paid. The train will become overcrowded, the company will lose money, and may eventually become bankrupt. Ticket officers probably get to recognise the signs of fare dodgers, for example – the ones who pretend to be asleep, who hold their thumb over the date of their ticket, who hide in the toilet as the officer comes past. A ticket officer will firstly try to prevent rogue passengers from coming on board and secondly will kick out any that he finds.

Your mind is just like a train. Rogue thoughts try to get on board and take up space. So just like a ticket officer inspects people getting on a train, you need to identify the thoughts trying to take root in your mind and throw them out if they are rogues. The ticket officer has to learn and recognise the *common characteristics* of rogues; similarly, we need to learn to recognise the *common characteristics* of negative thoughts. Before we turn to this, we must define some terms.

Absolute Truth vs Perceived Truth

There has been a recent tendency to believe that:

> "Whatever is true *for you*, is true."

This saying stems from "relativism"; a branch of philosophy that believes there is no such thing as absolute truth. They effectively believe:

> "The *absolute truth* is there is no such thing as *absolute truth*."

This does not make sense. Either Elvis is dead or alive. The *absolute truth* is that he is physically dead. Regardless of your belief, you cannot make him come alive again. An *Absolute truth* is the reality of the situation.

In contrast, a *perceived truth* is however you see a situation.

You may believe that Elvis is alive. That is your *perceived truth.*

- Absolute truth is the "reality of the situation"
- Perceived truth is "what you believe about the situation"

Even a colour, such as blue, has an absolute value. Pure blue is defined as RGB (0, 0, 255). Its frequency lies within 670–610Thz. Yes, each of our eyes may perceive pure blue differently – but that is due to our eye perception. There are absolute facts about the colour blue.

Our perception of reality cannot change reality. However, it may change the way we act.

Conscious Recall versus Subconscious Recall

Conscious recall is when previously stored information is retrieved, and we become aware of that information. For example, what is the missing number?

1 2 ? 4 5 6 7

You will consciously think 3.

Subconscious recall is when previously stored information is retrieved, and we are *not* aware of that information. For example, when you looked at the sequence of numbers above you will have subconsciously recognised "?" as a question mark. But you will not have actually thought, or verbalised "question mark" in your head. You will also have subconsciously thought "this is a sequence of numbers" and "these are numbers".

The term used for conscious recall is often referred to as "explicit memory". The term used for subconscious recall is "implicit memory". Jonathan K. Foster's brilliant book on the memory explains the difference as follows:

> "Suppose you heard a new song some time ago. Later, you might recall the words of the song, or recognise the words when you hear them again [conscious recall]. Alternatively, if you hear the song again, the words might sound familiar without your explicit recognising them [part subconscious recall]. Finally, your behaviour or mental state might be covertly influenced by the message of the song, without your having any sense of conscious recall, recognition or familiarity for the song itself [fully subconscious recall]."[19]

Often subconscious memories (implicit) start as conscious information (explicit). Information often fades from the conscious realm into the subconscious realm. As a child if you are repeatedly told that you are a failure, this may then recede into the subconscious. As an adult if you break a vase, you might not consciously think "I'm a failure", however, that thought may cross your subconscious mind and the associated feelings may surface.

Now that we have defined some terms, let us consider some of the ways in which thinking errors are stored. Lies can often masquerade as truths. If we can understand the characteristics of deceptive thoughts, it will be easier to identify them and challenge them before they steal our hope.

**The problem with deception,
is that we don't know when
we are being deceived.**

Conscious Doubt and Lies

The normal weight range for a 6ft tall girl aged 30 is between about 11 and 13 stone.

> "Jenny is 6ft tall and weighs 7 stone. Considerably underweight. Jess tells her she is fat!!"

Is this a lie? Of course it is. Jess tells Jenny that she is fat but Jenny is nowhere near being fat. If someone is underweight a lie like this is obvious. Extreme lies are obvious. However, the more subtle deceptions are the ones that can influence our mood. Doubt can make us susceptible to believing deceiving thoughts. It is much easier to believe a deceptive thought if it is subtle, said by someone who is closer to you, or there is an element of doubt to it.

> "Jenny is 6ft tall and weighs 13 stone. On the borderline between a healthy weight and overweight. Jess tells her she is fat!!"

Now, this is much more subtle – according to BMI mass 13 stone is on the upper end of a healthy weight for her height. A doubt will cross her mind "Am I fat?" and then she is more likely to believe a lie. Obviously, if Jenny knows that being 13 stone is perfectly healthy, and then Jess made such a comment, she would be less likely to believe it. So dealing with doubt is about establishing confidence in the truth.

Conscious Combinations: a truth with a lie

Conscious doubts or lies are one way to deceive someone, but when a truth is combined with a lie, it makes the lie much stronger because we are more likely to believe it.

> "Jenny is 6ft tall and weighs 20 stone. Considerably overweight. Jess tells her that nobody could ever love her because she is too fat!!"

Jenny is certain that she is fat and therefore makes the conclusion that she is unlovable. However, note that there are two statements here:

> Statement 1: I'm 20 stone and therefore fat.
> Statement 2: Nobody can love me because I'm fat.

The first statement is true. <u>The second is untrue</u>. But if Jenny doesn't separate them out, and if she believes the combination, then she falls for an overall lie. This is one of the most subtle lies we fall for. A truth or several truths in combination with a lie.

Separate out what you believe into smaller chunks and consider each one.

Subconscious Combinations: a truth with a hidden lie

In the previous example we have two statements on a conscious level: "I'm fat" and "I'm unlovable". However, in reality a lot of lies are on a subconscious level. There may be a forgotten or unknown element to what you believe. Part of a statement may be on a conscious level but the other on a subconscious level.

Let's say, as a child, Jenny's teacher said to Jenny that if she became fat, nobody would ever love her. Now Jenny might have completely forgotten what the teacher said on a conscious level. But she may have stored it as a subconscious memory.

As an adult Jenny is 6ft tall and weighs 20 stone – considerably overweight. Mark comes along and tells Jenny that she is fat. In reality, Mark has only made a true statement. However, when Jenny hears this she feels extremely low. Why would Jenny feel low hearing the truth? In reality, what Jenny does is combine the true statement that mark makes with the subconscious memory of what her teacher said. She doesn't actually consciously think the subconscious lie, but the combination of both triggers negative feelings. The overall effect is as follows:

Mark creates thought on a **conscious** level	I'm fat
Jenny recalls the teachers lie on a **subconscious** level	...therefore nobody can love me

Combining a conscious truth with a subconscious lie is the most dangerous form of deception. Jenny is low because she falls for the combination. On going to a counsellor she tells them "I'm depressed because I'm fat." The counsellor says, stop lying to yourself. Jenny replies: "I'm not lying, I am fat." What Jenny doesn't realise is that she is combining conscious and subconscious thoughts. The lie is effectively split between the conscious and subconscious levels.

During depression a person may not be actually saying a lie out loud, or consciously thinking a lie, but subconsciously they may be believing a deceptive thought. It may help to separate out what you believe into smaller chunks and see if you are subconsciously adding further chunks, then consider each one and how they interact.

Ultimately, we do not necessarily need to know what the underlying issue or thought is, though it *can* help. Digging into the past can be extremely exhausting and so much time analysing problems can lead to paralysis of analysis. Rather, it is better to use the replacement theory. Soak ourselves in truth, instil hope, train ourselves to observe our thoughts, and be more self-aware. This ultimately is a better solution.

So we don't necessarily need to find out that Jenny believes the lie:

> "I'm fat therefore nobody can love and accept me"

We simply need to instil the truth:

> "Fat people are loveable. There are lots of fat people who have extremely good relationships and partners. The truth is that you can always lose weight. That your body doesn't define you as a person."

Subconscious combinations can be one of the most powerful forms of deception. Assumptive combinations are also extremely deceptive.

Stored Beliefs versus On-the-fly Beliefs (Assumptions)

Some memories we store, and others we create on-the-fly by using fragments of stored information; these known as assumptions.

Stored Belief

A "Stored belief" is normally stored as a single chunk of information. For example, what is the capital of England? "London". You already had this belief stored in your memory. In this instance, when the question is asked, you search your memory for the answer, then retrieve it to the conscious realm.

This can be represented as follows:

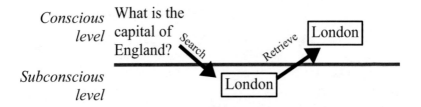

In this example the retrieval happened quickly. Sometimes our memories are slower. For instance, it may take a while to remember someone's name.

Stored beliefs are not necessarily objectively/absolutely true. Stored beliefs may be real to the person but not reflect true reality. I've highlighted the word in grey to show the following is not objectively true.

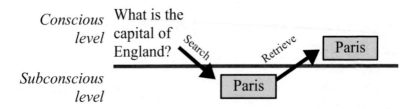

Stored beliefs are not necessarily geographical facts. They can beliefs about ourselves, others or the world. Which of the following do you think are true:

- "My identity is defined by my work."
- "My identity is defined by my relationships."
- "Nobody likes me."
- "Everyone loves my shirt."
- "I'll never get married."
- "When a woman strokes her hair she's flirting."
- "When someone doesn't smile back at me, they don't

like me."

- "Climate change will destroy the planet."

Of course, as mentioned earlier, stored beliefs aren't always retrieved – sometimes they remain in the subconscious and affect our emotions and actions without us realising.

In the cases of Jenny. Her belief in each case is a "stored belief" regardless of whether it is retrieved:

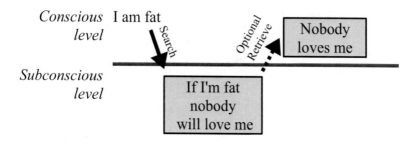

On-the-fly beliefs (assumptions)
In contrast, we can create on-the-fly assumptions by using fragments of stored information.

Assumptions are when we try to add information in the gaps using all the knowledge we have available. What is the following picture of?

Perhaps you think it is of a face. Perhaps you think it is a coastline on a map. Perhaps you think it is an inkblot. All of those are incorrect assumptions. In reality, it is some coffee spilt on a piece of paper. Maybe you assumed correctly?

When we assume we try our best to draw on what we have available in our memory to make the best sense of what is going on.

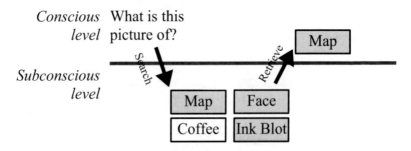

Now that I have given you the answer, your memory will create a stored belief. "This is a coffee stain". In this way, assumptions normally only happen during our first exposure to something, or until we know the truth. Sometimes we will never discover the objective/absolute truth or reality. If I hadn't told you that it was a coffee stain, your assumption would have continued regardless of whether your assumption was objectively true. A more potent example of assumption is as follows:

Poppy loves Kyle. Kyle likes Poppy but has never asked her out on a date. Kyle decides he would like to get to know Poppy. On Friday he arranges to host a party at his house. He invites Poppy but she doesn't turn up. Kyle assumes that Poppy doesn't like him. So Kyle never approaches Poppy again. He sees her in the street a week later and crosses to the other side to avoid her.

Poppy liked Kyle so why did Poppy not come to the party? It might have been that:

- She felt nervous.
- She'd had a telephone call about her grandmother dying.
- Her telephone had broken.
- She was ill.
- Kyle sent the message to the wrong number.

Kyle does not have any stored belief about Poppy before he hosts the party. He doesn't believe "Poppy doesn't like me". When Poppy doesn't show up, he doesn't retrieve a single chunk of information. What he does is create an "on-the-fly belief (assumption)" from a mixture of subconscious beliefs:

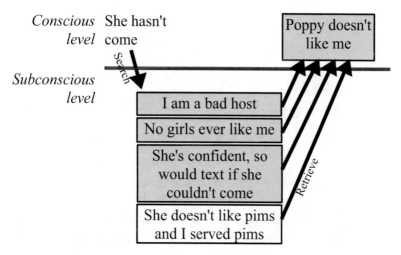

Mind reading is a big stumbling block for humans because we draw a lot of incorrect conclusions.

All humans do it. We sit there assuming that the other person is thinking some negative thought about us when we are ninety-five percent of the time wrong.

> "She hasn't come to the party because
> she doesn't like me."

Why do we attempt to fill in the gap? Why do we make negative assumptions? Why can't we stop at the fact "She didn't come to the party"?

Note here that if he'd believed "Poppy doesn't like me" that wouldn't be as potent as "She didn't come to the party, therefore she doesn't like me". The former is a conscious lie. The second combines truth with a lie, and is therefore much more deceptive.

> **"Assumptions are dangerous things"**
> *Agatha Christie*

Bad assumptions are often magnifications of already accepted lies. Here Kyle already has three negative "stored beliefs":

1. I am a bad host.
2. No girls ever like me.
3. She's confident, so would text if she couldn't come.

If Kyle knew 100% that he was a fantastic host, that girls do like him, and that Poppy was actually shy – he may never have made the assumption he did. Mind-reading assumptions don't just come out of nowhere – they are normally manifestations of existing deceptive thoughts.

Furthermore, you can actually reinforce these negative beliefs in the process of creating assumptions. For example:

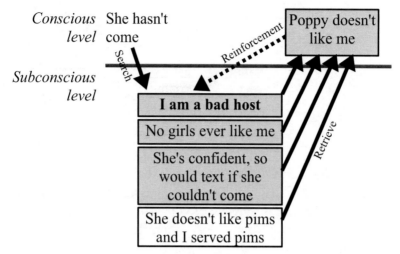

By coming to the assumption that Poppy doesn't like him, Kyle reinforces one of the underlying beliefs – that he is a bad host. This underlying belief becomes stronger (hence we mark it in bold type). Often people only tend to pay attention to the information that confirms their belief. This is called confirmation bias. Confirmation bias can reinforce a positive or negative belief.

**Assumptions stem from and
often reinforce existing beliefs**

**"Confirmation bias is the most
effective way to go on living a lie."**
Criss Jami

Note here that after Kyle has had this initial assumption he will store the new thought as a "stored belief". When he sees her in the street he retrieves this stored belief directly rather than creating an "on-the-fly belief" again.

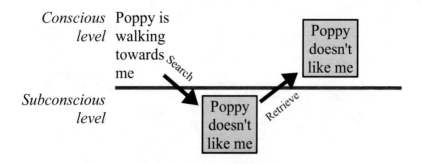

Both "Stored beliefs" and "On-the-fly beliefs (assumptions)" are dangerous. The key to minimising assumptions is making sure you have a healthy view of yourself, and continue to remember truths until they become a reflex action.

Be careful not to assume

Feelings that lie

Feelings _can_ be a type of deception. Feelings are not facts; they _can_ lie to us. Remember the story of Joe, Sandra and the dead cat (p.55). Sandra's feelings did not reflect the reality of the situation; it wasn't her cat.

**Feelings are real, but they do not
always reflect the reality of the situation.**

Also consider the story of Poppy and Kyle (p.134). Kyle assumed Poppy didn't like him. His feelings weren't based on the objective truth. He acted on an assumption and his feelings, so consequently never found out the truth that Poppy did indeed like him.

Because our feelings sometimes lie to us, we should avoid making major decisions when we are down. I remember a friend who had a particular disagreement with her boss and she was tempted to throw in the towel and leave her job that day. Because she was particularly stressed, I suggested that she took a couple of days off as sick-leave and get a note from the doctor. A couple of days rest would help her think through her problems rationally. She was still suffering from shock and if she'd reacted in the moment, she might have done something she came to regret later.

Dormant/Latent Lies

Negative thoughts may lie dormant for many years without manifesting any problems. This is one of the reasons why we have to be careful what information we absorb through our senses.

When Greg was young he watched a film about burglars entering a house, stealing all the jewellery, and then going into the bedroom and beating up the owners before leaving. He said that he was not affected by the violence. Twenty years later someone broke into his house and he became extremely fearful that the burglars would come into his room and beat him up.

Experts sometimes say that violence in films doesn't affect people; usually saying, specifically that we don't become violent by watching it. This mostly *appears* to be true. However, what the so-called experts are missing, is that information can lie dormant for many years without ever having an effect. Greg didn't believe what he had watched had affected him; he had never faced a situation with a burglar, and therefore assumed that no negative thoughts or fears had resulted from what he'd watched when he was younger. Nonetheless, he did unknowingly believe the lie that burglars beat up owners, and this made him fearful. The dormant lie only became apparent when the memory was stimulated.

The Characteristics of Lies

Unhealthy thoughts have characteristics, such as the following:

- They over-generalise.
- They tend to be extreme. This is sometimes referred to as "black and white" thinking.
- They are "demanding" – harsh rigid expectations are made that forget to take into account that we are not perfect and are works in progress.
- They assume that everything is a catastrophe.
- They tend to draw the worst conclusions.

These unhealthy thoughts might come with particular associated words. The following are common:

- **Superlatives:** A superlative in the English language is when there is an extreme adjective. For example, "tallest" is the superlative where "tall" is the adjective. Watch out for words such as: *worst, ugliest, biggest,* and *most.*

- **Strong auxiliaries**: An auxiliary is a secondary verb. Strong ones are common in thinking errors, such as: *must, should,* and *will.*

- **General pronouns:** Pronouns are the people involved in a sentence. In particular, look out for the general ones, as follows: *everyone, everybody, nobody, people* (not strictly a pronoun).

> **Watch out for superlatives, strong auxiliaries, and general pronouns.**

The following words are common in negative thought life:

"Nobody. Nobody ever phones me."

"Always. I always mess up."

"Never. I never get an opportunity."

"I'm a. I'm an idiot."

"Must. I must get this job."

"I have to. I have to look good."

"Should. I should have spent more money on."

"Ought to. I ought to be successful by now."

"People. People are always ignoring me."

"If. If I got this one thing sorted I would be happy"

"By now. I should have found a wife by now."

"Everyone. Everyone thinks I'm an idiot."

"All. All my work colleagues ignore me."

Labelling Lies

As humans we have a tendency to label things. Why? Labelling probably occurs due to the simplification of language during communication. This is particularly evident when a parent communicates with a child. For example:

Three different toy cars are respectively coloured burgundy, scarlet and crimson. The parent cannot ask "Do you like the burgundy, scarlet, or crimson car the best?" This is simply because the child doesn't know these shades. Instead the parent asks "Which of the three <u>red</u> cars do you like the best?" The child responds by pointing to his favourite car.

Because the child doesn't know the shades burgundy, scarlet and crimson, the parent had to express these shades of colour in another way. She simplified the information using the word "red". We often simplify, categorise and label in order to communicate ideas. This simplification is referred to more in my second book.

Labelling happens in many areas of life. In particular, we tend to label ourselves. We may label ourselves as a failure, success, ugly, fat, beautiful etc. One of the biggest mistakes we make with valuing ourselves is that we tend to value our worth according to our circumstances and on what others think of us. We tend to value ourselves by comparing ourselves to other people. This is fruitless. Why are other people's labels and opinions so important?

Another problem that we fall prey to is trying to put a value on our worth based on the present moment rather than assessing our worth over a longer period.

> A caterpillar climbs up a leaf, looks at a reflection of himself in a water droplet. He stops and sighs and thinks to himself. "Look at me stuck here eating green leaves every single day. This is mundane. I'm a failure. I'm so lonely, I have no friends. What is the point? Life is a waste of time. I'm ugly too. There's no hope. If only I could be like one of those butterflies over there in the meadow. Look at them - they are free, have got friends, and they are so beautiful. If only. Life is pointless. I'll never be like them. What is the point?"

Of course, the caterpillar is just looking at the here and now and has forgotten that he will eventually become a beautiful butterfly. We have a tendency to focus on all the problems now and the successes of others – but remember we are at different stages of life. A lot of very successful people went through difficult times. Why do people label themselves all day long when they are going to change anyway? Labels are static, we are not.

There is a tendency to walk around with old labels on. When a drug addict stops taking drugs would he continue to tell everyone he is a drug addict? No, well at least he shouldn't do. So why is it that people who believe they failed at school continue to call themselves a failure when they are no longer at school. Why do people keep the labels? You're a failure. No you're not. You used to have periods of failure and disappointment. But you can't be a failure, you haven't finished your life yet. You could be a wowing success in years to come. We are not a product of our past.

You can't label yourself because you are forever changing. Don't label.

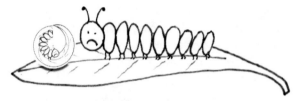

You may feel like a caterpillar now.

But caterpillars turn into butterflies.

Another huge problem with labels is that they can become self-fulfilling prophecies.

> Fred sits all day in front of the television and doesn't do any work. His mother shouts at him: "Oh, you are so lazy". This kind of statement attacks the identity of someone and potentially reinforces it. Over time Fred starts to believe he is indeed a lazy person and it becomes a self-fulfilling prophecy. Alternatively his mother could have said "You're not a lazy person, so why are you behaving in a lazy manner." This kind of comment is targeted at Fred's behaviour rather than his identity and therefore it actually encourages Fred not to be lazy. Over time if he believes he is not lazy, his behaviour will start to come in line with what he believes about his identity.

We need to be extra careful to separate our behaviour from who we are. Even if you "fail" at something, that doesn't mean you are a "failure".

We all deceive ourselves to a certain extent. Everyone has some unhealthy labels that they've given themselves; these can be called our "core beliefs". They need to be uprooted and replaced by healthy truths. Depression occurs when thoughts about yourself have become deceptive. In order to identify these deceptions we need to ask questions and keep drilling down to the core beliefs by asking why those thoughts exist. We need to replace the deceptions with the truth.

False Positive Beliefs
Sometimes we have beliefs which we think are positive, healthy and true, but we may have made assumptions or have subconscious beliefs that may render what we deem to be true

as actually false. These can be considered as "false positive beliefs". Pride is an example of this. Let's look a few examples:

Example 1
A teacher thinks: "The children in this class are stupid. My children are much better."

The clause "My children are much better" might seem positive, healthy and true. However, consider the underlying assumption and subconscious lie:-

Assumption:	"All children should be clever. We all have the same opportunities to learn. We all have the ability to be clever. They just haven't tried hard enough."
Subconscious lie:	"Stupid people are not valuable. My children's intelligence means that they are more valuable than other human beings. Value is measured by intelligence."

Example 2
A rich teenager thinks: "Look at him. He doesn't have the latest Apple iPhone."

Assumption:	"We all have the same disposable finances. We should all be able to afford an Apple iPhone. We should all like the iPhone."
Subconscious lie:	"What we own defines our significance and value."

Common Lies

We are much more similar than you think. A lot of us have similar negative thoughts so this is one reason we shouldn't feel embarrassed to tell someone. Keeping things secret is not recommended. Do you recognise any of the following common lies?

- I'll never amount to anything.
- No one loves or cares for me.
- My situation is hopeless, I see no way out but to die.
- I'm stupid, I'm dumb, I'm ugly.
- I'm a mistake.
- Life is the pits.
- My future is hopeless.
- Nobody can help me.
- I'm worthless and would be better off dead.
- I have no value and no meaningful purpose for being here.

Ruminating Lies

Another common characteristic of lies is that they are often repetitious. When we think something over and over again in psychological terms it is called "rumination". Rumination is defined as:

> "Obsessive thoughts concerning extreme,
> recurring ideas or concepts that interrupt
> other types of cognitive actions"[20]

Just like a record can get stuck, our thoughts can get stuck on one particular thing. For example, it might be that the person thinks "I'll never get a job". That thought is played over and over in their head. Notice the superlative "Never". If you get something you are constantly saying or thinking to yourself, it might be worth stepping back and analysing those thoughts.

Repeating thoughts and feelings about yourself that are not true establishes mental strongholds over a period of time. If we ruminate on and rehearse negative thoughts, they will make depression worse.

Excessive talking about problems can be unhelpful too. Getting your problems off your chest is not always getting them off your chest. If you are repeating them to someone – you are effectively ruminating on them out loud and could be reinforcing those ideas and simply engraving those thoughts even deeper in your mind. Make sure that you are not simply replaying negative thoughts but dealing with them.

Perspective Lies

In our discovery so far we have found out that a lot of depression results from incorrect thinking, a lack of truth, and the inability to memorise these truths. Whether it is an incorrect thought or simply a lack of knowledge, both could be considered a truth deficiency. Incorrect perspectives can also be considered as lies.

Consider a physical box. One side is black and the other sides are all white. Imagine someone is sitting with the black face in front of them but they cannot see the other sides. If they comment and say "This is a very dark box" their statement is incorrect based on their perspective.

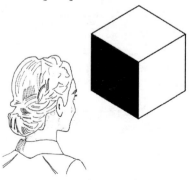

The person's perspective is incorrect because they are deficient in truth in some area. This could be as follows:

- They believe or assume that boxes have sides with all the same colour.

- They don't realise they can rotate the box to look at the other sides.

- They don't realise that they can move themselves around the box.

- They thought it was a flat two-dimensional piece of card and didn't realise it was a box.

If they knew that boxes didn't necessarily have sides the same colour, they knew they could rotate the box, they knew it was a box and not a flat object, and they had observed it from more than one side, they would not have in incorrect perspective. So problems with perspective come from a lack of knowledge.

People don't respond to events in themselves but respond to their interpretations of events. We bring our assumptions and previous knowledge and combine them with what is going on. After the abolition of slavery in America, the event did not necessarily set everyone free. Some slave owners didn't tell their workers that they were now free to go. They thought that if they could get the slaves to think they were still slaves, the legal proclamation wouldn't affect them. They kept the truth from the slaves; that they were free to go and no longer had to be slaves. However, because the slaves didn't know the truth, they continued to be slaves.

Your perspective can change everything

148

Perspective is very important when dealing with life. The following areas are often ignored when looking at problems:

- Time – How do we view this problem in the overall context of time?

- Money – How do we look at this problem through the context of money?

- Emotion – What are the emotional costs? What are the emotional benefits?

- Character – How does this improve my character?

- Opportunities – How does this open up new opportunities?

- External – How does this problem fit in with other people?

- Parental – How would a child view this?

- Language – Are there different words to describe this?

Time:
What do you now think of the problems you had five years ago? You may think, why did I worry about that so much? What about the problems you have now? What will you think of it in twenty years time? Today's problems will probably be forgotten in a year's time – they'll seem so much smaller in the grand scheme of life.

Years ago I had a nasty pain in my legs and found it difficult to walk. All I could focus on was the pain. At the time I worried about the future and not being able to walk properly, worried about being prematurely old. But I got better. What do I think of that problem now? Nothing. How big was the problem in the grand scheme of life – "small". But how big did it appear at the time - "big". When you get to the end of your life, what will you think of the problem that you're experiencing right now?

149

What is permanent? All things are temporary. This too will pass.

External:
I am one person in a large world. We tend to look at problems internally. We can tend to be harder on ourselves than other people. If a friend was going through the identical problem you are facing, what would you say to them? Sometimes asking friends for their viewpoint on a problem can also help you to refocus your perspective.

Parental:
If a child was asked to draw a garden and it didn't look particularly good, what would you say to them? Would you say "That's terrible, you might as well give up, you'll never amount to anything"? Probably not – and yet we can have a tendency to treat ourselves worse than we would treat a child. How would you treat a child if they had the same problems you are experiencing now?

Language:
Our English language is rich in words. Some words carry negative connotations and we can be quick to use them. Sometimes there is a more positive alternative. Consider the words: "Perfectionist" versus "Meticulous", "Fearful" versus "Cautious", "Worried" versus "Concerned". Often we talk about "Problems" rather than "Challenges". If you start to view your problems as challenges, it can give you a more positive outlook and instil more hope.

Start to see problems as challenges

Challenges shape us if we overcome them. Challenges can send us in a new direction which allows us to explore new avenues and discover ourselves. For example, when I left university all I wanted to do was be a film composer – if I'd

150

had instant success I may have ended up on that treadmill of life and not explored what other possibilities there were – I probably would never have become a film director or written this book.

We often talk about struggling with something. Struggle is not necessarily a bad thing. Do people climb up Everest without struggling? Of course not, but why not reword this as "perseverance?" Perseverance builds character. We often need to persevere to succeed as suggested in the following quote:

> **"Success is the ability to go from one failure to another with no loss of enthusiasm"**
> *Winston Churchill*

Perseverance is an important part of dealing with challenges. If we see problems as challenges we are likely to persevere, if we see them as problems we are more likely to give up. Perseverance can give us enjoyment.

What if all your dreams came true tomorrow – then what?

Could you imagine a life where all your dreams came true? Let's say you wanted to win 10 Oscars as an actress and be a multimillionaire. Let's say I could snap my fingers and by next Wednesday all of those dreams came true. Then what? What would you do on Thursday? Sometimes a dream slowly fulfilled can be more rewarding than if it just lands at your feet. A businessman who slowly earns a million will probably enjoy the process and the money more than the person who inherits a million.

When you want to get somewhere quickly, a road diversion can be frustrating, especially when a motorway is closed and you have to go down the back roads. However, if you are not in a hurry, following a diversion can actually be enjoyable because you discover new roads and scenery that you may never have seen before. This is a variation in your route. Rather than see problems as roadblocks – we can start to view them as diversions, or better still, variations in life. We can often discover and experience new things and our character can often change as a result of variations. Note that road diversions often frustrate us because we are in a hurry.

When coming to a road diversion would you ever stop your car, get out and get angry with the workmen, try to move the cones out the way and try to argue about driving down the normal route? No, you'd be wasting time. You'll get to your destination more quickly by simply recognising that this route is closed and by following the diversion signs. Also, if you constantly get annoyed at the roadblock you'll be thinking angry thoughts all the way around the diverted route and this could mean you miss out on new or interesting scenery. So the language we use is important in keeping our levels of hope up.

**Problems can enrich your life because
they send you in a new direction.**

**Don't get stuck at a roadblock.
If you can't solve the problem,
see the problem as diverting you in a new
direction and enjoy the scenic route.**

See problems as challenges.

See struggle as perseverance.

See diversions as variations.

Change your language.

Character:
We tend not to view things through the perspective of developing character. Who are the people you like most? Why? Is it because of their talents, bank balance, possessions or character? On the whole, we tend to like people the most because of their characters. So we should value character development more. Setbacks in life can send us in new directions to discover new things and help build character, and this in turn can make us happier and more attractive to others. We learn a lot about ourselves in the hard times.

A mistake is only a failure if you fail to learn from it, and if your character remains the same. What can you learn from what you have gone through? What hidden benefits do these challenges have?

Memory Stimulation / Triggers

In the last section we discussed how hope can be stolen from a lack of truth. We looked at how deception and lies are stored as negative memories. Next we turn to memory stimulation. Let's consider our equation again:-

**HOPE = TRUTH + STIMULATION +
MEMORY CHOICE/RECALL +
MEMORY COMBINATION**

A lot of our thought-life is triggered externally. Memories don't normally suddenly infiltrate us – they come because of an association, image, sound, smell etc.

What comes to mind when I introduce the word "Popcorn"? Your mind probably visualises the cinema, a film you watched recently, or a film you want to watch. For most people the word "Popcorn" does not stimulate image and memories of the bathroom because most people do not eat popcorn in the bath. Remember, feelings are triggered by memories. Memories can be triggered by a range of things, so it is important to notice what triggers both happy and bad memories. As mentioned earlier, Finzi's Clarinet Concerto always triggers memories of unrequited love and feelings that accompany that. I tend to be careful when listening to it – otherwise it can drag me into a bad frame of mind. On the contrary, cyclamen flowers trigger good thoughts because they remind me of a positive dream I once had.

Do you know what images and words trigger your negative thoughts and feelings? It is a good idea to start to notice what triggers your emotions; get to know what stimulates your memory. It might be worth avoiding bad triggers or better still creating new associations.

One particular pub, which I occasionally pass, reminds me of a negative event. I could avoid driving past that place, but if I'm not careful I could end up avoiding the whole world. If, however, I can think of a positive enjoyable event in the bar, and if I keep thinking about it, it is possible to stamp out the negative association by replacing it with a positive memory.

When I was on holiday in Tenby I had a minor accident in my car. It now has a small dent. Every time I think of Tenby I am reminded of the dent in my car, and my actions. What I need to do is start to re-associate the word Tenby with a new positive memory. I have some nice memories of seeing lovely cloud formations on the beach. I need to establish a new connection "Tenby = Clouds" and not "Tenby = Car dent".

Self-awareness is key in helping battle depression. Knowing key triggers and thoughts that set you into a downward spiral can take time to find and understand – but in the long run is worth it.

One trigger for me is lying in bed in the morning. If I lie in bed too long, I start to ruminate. Now I tend to get up when I wake up. You may have particular triggers or situations that start negative thinking patterns. Some common triggers for increased anxiety and depression are as follows.

- Lying in bed.
- Spending too much time on your own.
- Waiting in a queue or for a bus.
- Looking at a bank balance (that doesn't mean you should avoid it, but be careful to protect your emotions whilst you do it)
- Opening post (that doesn't mean you should avoid it, but be careful to protect your emotions whilst you do it).
- Sitting in traffic jams.
- Leaving late for scheduled appointments or work.
- Extremely overcast days.
- Social Media e.g. Facebook.
- Negative newspaper articles.

Not only can we notice what triggers unhealthy thoughts but also learn to recognise what stimulates positive thoughts. Sometimes if we've had an enjoyable experience, writing these down to remind ourselves can be useful.

Writing down your stories of how you've overcome something is also key. We are naturally more forgetful than we realise. Let's say Jim overcame his financial problems. By writing down how he overcame his problems when he is faced with the same problem, he can return to what he has written and that will encourage him and give him hope that he can deal with similar situations. I know a lady who keeps a book of all the good things that have gone well in life. Whenever she is tempted to feel low she gets out her book and all the positive stories help lift her mood.

Summary

1. Your imagination is key to gaining hope.

2. Hope = Truth + Stimulation + Memory Choice/Recall + Memory Combination

3. Hope is knowing the truth and then actively remembering it until it becomes an automatic reflex.

4. Have I been in this situation before? What was the outcome? Has anyone else been in this situation – how did they resolve it?

5. Get advice.

6. Try different not harder.

7. Be patient.

8. Lies steal our hope.

9. Lies fall into various categories:

   - Conscious Doubt and Lies

   - Conscious Combinations: a truth with a lie.

   - Subconscious Combinations: a truth with a hidden lie.

   - On-the-fly Beliefs (Assumptions)

   - Feelings that lie to us.

   - Dormant/Latent lies.

10. Lies have various characteristics:

   - Lies use particular language e.g. "Should" "Must" "By now" "Never".

   - Lies often label.

156

- Lies can be disguised as false positive beliefs (pride).

- Lies are common.

- Lies tend to get stuck in our minds (ruminate).

- Lies often occur from having an incorrect perspective.

11. Start seeing problems as challenges.

12. Look out for unhelpful words.

13. Your memories are stimulated by previous associations you've made, so be careful what associations you make.

14. Identify your positive and negative triggers.

CHANGE YOUR THINKING - PART 3
EMOTIONS – GENERAL OUTLOOK

In "Change your thinking - part 2" we dealt with some general characteristics of your thinking; how truth, the ability to recognise deceptive thoughts, and the memory, all affect our levels of hope. In this next chapter we will look at various emotions and how they impact our lives. Each of these sections could be a book in itself; they are here to get you thinking about each topic.

Anger and Frustration

"Depression is anger turned inward"[21]

There is a large element of truth to this statement. A lot of us become angry at ourselves or others when we fail to meet imposed deadlines, standards, or have our wills crossed. How does anger form and how can we deal with it? Let us look at an example:

Harriet wanted a new dress for her birthday. She spent hours searching through catalogues and chose three at different price ranges, respectively £30, £60 and £90. She then submitted them to her mother as a birthday list. On her birthday she opened up her present and found her mother had bought a sleeping bag instead. She was furious and angry with her mother.

Why was Harriet angry? Firstly, she'd spent hours ruminating on what she wanted. If she'd spent two minutes browsing through the catalogues, she'd probably not have been so disappointed. Secondly, her will was crossed – she didn't get what she wanted. And thirdly, she had a couple of unhealthy beliefs. She believed that she deserved to get what she wanted, and she also believed she knew what was best for herself. She didn't consider that her mother could have had a better option.

Why did the mother buy a sleeping bag? The mother had bought a sleeping bag for Harriet because she had a sleepover in a couple of weeks and her old sleeping bag was too small and unfashionable. She knew that her daughter would feel inferior at the sleepover in a couple of weeks time and wanted to make her feel happy.

It might be useful to consider the following questions:

- If you spent very little time ruminating about what you wanted, how angry would you become?
- If you spent more time ruminating on what others want, rather than what you want, how angry would you be with yourself?
- Think of the last time you got angry, how much time had you spent ruminating about what you wanted?
- If you never had your will crossed, what kind of person would you be?
- What do you deserve? Why?
- If you went through life feeling you deserved nothing and saw everything as a bonus, or added benefit, would you ever get angry?
- Do you always know best? Are there other people who might have better opinions or make better suggestions?

Another reason why Harriet may have become angry is that she felt she had wasted time looking at the catalogue. Because she ruminated for ages on what to buy she was potentially more angry than if she had only spent a couple of minutes flicking through the catalogue.

Most events in life have a process and an end goal. For example, when practising the violin for a concert the process is practising the violin, and the end goal is playing in the concert. When we fail to achieve the end goal, we may get angry. We often think this is because we didn't achieve the end result. Unknowingly, however, what can actually be more upsetting to us is that we feel we've wasted time, energy and resource. In this way, anger can often stem from a sense of what we feel we've wasted (time, money, energy, resource), rather than what we've failed to achieve.

We walk two miles to get to a restaurant and we find it is closed. It probably isn't the fact the restaurant is closed that angers us the most – the anger is more likely to be that we feel as if we've just wasted 40 minutes walking there. Our car needs fixing and it will cost £600; what angers us most is not that the car is broken, but we feel as if we've wasted £600 which we could have spent on something else. When we compete in a race and don't come first, what probably angers us most is the feeling that we have more potential and ability and aren't living up to it. We feel we are wasting our ability and talents. We spend ages trying to date a girl and it doesn't work out; what probably angers us most is that we feel we've missed other opportunities or wasted time.

Anger often stems from a feeling that we've wasted, time, money, our talents, or potential.

Anger is poor waste management

If I were to buy a new camera at £900, I might spend ages looking at all the possibilities because that might be considered a large amount. However, when choosing a pen in a shop, I will just pick one – because if it goes wrong, or I don't like it, I can simply go back and buy another one. Sometimes I feel as if I'm wasting hours and hours researching

160

what to buy. I'm fearful of wasting money – but ironically I waste a lot of time.

Wasted Time

Why do we fear wasting time? Is it because we are concerned more about quantity than quality? Hadyn wrote 106 symphonies and Rachmaninov wrote 3 beautiful symphonies. Nobody is complaining that Rachmaninov didn't write 106 symphonies.

The average life expectancy of people in the Middle Ages was about 30. Even if you work at 50% efficiency, you will achieve just as much in a lifetime as back then. Also, in those times people spent a lot of time simply surviving. Boredom didn't exist for them; it's a 'modern' concept. The average westerner no longer has to wash clothes by hand, pluck the chicken, dig up the potatoes etc. In all history we are the most time rich. We have huge amounts of time for ourselves and yet for some reason we seem to demand more and more from every second of the day. I doubt if people in the Middle Ages worried much about wasting time. Ironically the more time we have, the more we are fearful of wasting time.

We get angry for wasting time because we are rich in time

Do you see the clock as a countdown – every second closer to death? Or do you see every second of the clock as an added second to your life – a bonus? What about all the other benefits that we might overlook? The time we spent walking to the restaurant was additional time exercising. What about the time we spent researching what to buy, or the time Harriet spent looking at the catalogue? Perhaps she learnt more about what she liked – her preferences in life.

161

Wasted Money
All of us make mistakes in life with money, some on a small scale, and some on a larger scale. None of us like it. It might be something as simple as buying a pen that failed to work, or something more concerning, such as a long haul flight that we missed and consequently had to buy another ticket. Obviously, our financial status may alter the degree to which mistakes affects us. A millionaire who buys the wrong TV and wished he had bought a different one, can simply go out and buy another. Someone who is poor who has saved up to buy a TV and then made a mistake, cannot simply go out and purchase another, unless there is some kind of refund policy.

How much time can you afford browsing the internet? How much time can you afford looking at catalogues? Have you considered the cost of your time? Research can be important but when does it become imbalanced? Let's say you lived in medieval times and you want to buy a plough.

There is one blacksmith in town and he has two ploughs for sale. How difficult is the choice? How much time do you spend making the choice? How angry will you get if you choose the wrong one? Now fast forward. You want to buy a tractor for your farm. On the internet there are hundreds of different makes and models with different options? How difficult is it to make the choice? How much time do you spend making the choice? How angry will you get if you choose the wrong one?

We get angry for wasting money.
The abundance of choice and time taken
have contributed to this!

Count your blessings.
You have so much choice.

What if you do buy the wrong thing? Have you wasted that money? Especially when you can't go out and buy an alternative.

We make decisions based on what we know at the time. In hindsight we may have more information. How can you blame yourself for something when you couldn't see the outcome, or didn't have the information at the time of making the decision to make the best judgement? Don't hold yourself responsible for something you are not responsible for. If a holiday in a sun-baked country ends up being deluged with rain, you are not responsible for the weather. Disappointments will happen. It's not a question of preventing them, it's a question of how we respond to them. Forgive yourself. You are human. All humans make mistakes. Life is an adventure. We have to take risks. Risks cannot be successful 100% of the time but also realise that not all risks will end in failure. So don't let your disappointment prevent you from being adventurous in the future. Are you someone who never makes mistakes?

Wasted Potential
All of us have a deep longing to be significant; therefore, if we feel we have a potential in a certain area of life that is not being used to its full extent, we can get angry. Firstly, it is really important to understand that you have the potential to succeed in many different areas of life. Secondly, to realise that if you only succeeded in one of these areas, it might be potentially dangerous. Let me explain.

Jim is born as an extremely talented carpenter. He can sculpt 5 extremely beautiful tables each week; working seven day weeks and from 8am until 10pm every day. Let's say he kept up this rate from the age of 15 to 65. He has the potential to create 13,000 tables in his lifetime. Let's say he decides to get married and have children. If he spends a couple of hours each day with his children and has a day off at the weekend, he would either have to downgrade the quality of his tables, or he would have to reduce his output. In either of those instances Jim is no longer living up to his potential as a carpenter, because he would no longer be able to produce 13,000 tables. If Jim did indeed try to continue to live up to this potential, of creating 13,000 tables, he would be heading for a mental breakdown, put his family at risk, or face burnout. Consequently, he would not realise his potential to be a great father or a relaxed person.

Mozart was considered a genius and his output is astonishing. It is highly likely that Mozart died of an infection, but perhaps he caught this infection because he overworked himself and, as a result, became more susceptible to the infection. Perhaps he felt he had to live up to his potential and died of burnout.

Numerous people try to live up to their potential in one particular area of their lives. However, in doing so, they end up neglecting other areas. For example, a great banker who is a terrible father. Or a great father who is a terrible banker. Realise that you have more than one area of potential. You have the potential to succeed in many different areas of life, *but not all*.

Dealing with anger:

Recycle waste
As mentioned, anger can stem from what we feel we have wasted. How valuable is a tin can after you have eaten the contents? You may consider it as waste, useless, and insignificant. However, it is not. Tin cans can be recycled, melted down into car parts, bicycle parts, home appliances or more tin cans. A tin can is not waste if it is recycled. It is the same with your emotions, experiences, time, money and potential. If you start to recycle your emotional waste it can be useful for other things.

**A tin can is not waste unless you fail
to recycle it; recycle your emotions.**

Focus on the present

Most of our desires are based on the future. When we focus on
the present it can help divert our thoughts away from any
unmet desires; meaning we are less likely to become angry.
For example, if you were practising mindfulness, such as just
enjoying the colours of the sunset, it would be much harder to
become angry in the first place.

Focus on others

One of the most effective ways to diminish anger is to spend
less or no time ruminating on what we want, and spend more
time ruminating on what others want. As we focus on helping
others it will diminish the chances of becoming angry. This is
because anger often arises from having <u>own</u> goals blocked. If
we aren't focusing on our <u>own</u> goals, there will be less
potential for them to become blocked.

In addition, focusing on others is, in effect, a type of
mindfulness. It will help get our eyes off the future and onto
the present.

Hope can be found in helping others; in particular, giving help
to people in situation similar to ours.

Compare the two answers to the question "What will you have
achieved in five years time?"

1. I would like to have bought a boat and a nice car.
2. I would like to have bought one of my friends a boat
   and another friend a nice car.

Which one fills you with the most hope? If you focused your

efforts on the first how angry would you become if you didn't achieve it? Would you become more or less angry if you failed to meet the second ambition?

Spend less time ruminating about what you want and you will have less potential to get angry. Instead spend more time ruminating on what you can do for others.

Anger already aflame

There are two ways to deal with anger. Firstly, try to stop it in the first place. Or secondly, deal with the aftermath. Ideally, the quicker the problem is dealt with the better. The longer anger is left to fester, the more corrosive it becomes. So forgive quickly.

Who is the person you most become angry with? Perhaps it is yourself? This is fairly normal. I've heard phrases like "Stop being so hard on yourself!" For many, this doesn't work because it suggests that will power alone will make this happen. Simply telling ourselves to be more compassionate and forgiving to ourselves will often fail to work. Compassion comes from self-awareness. A TV advert could tell you to give £5 a month to orphans in Africa, but you can seldom force yourself to have compassion. If you are really able to understand what someone is going through, that is when you really start to feel compassion.

In order to be compassionate with yourself, you have to be more self-aware. Here are some more common anger problems:

- "I should have finished this by now" - Why - then what? Are you aiming for quality or quantity?

- "I'm too slow" - Compared to whom? What are the benefits of going slowly?

- "I should have" - How can you act upon something you didn't already have any information or experience of?

- "If I had gone down a different road I could have" - But what have you gained from this road?

Note the language used in the examples above. When we studied the characteristics of lies (on page 140) we identified certain common words such as "should have", "if only" etc. Anger frequently uses this kind of negative language.

"Anger is one letter short of danger"
Eleanor Roosevelt

Decision-Making

Decision-making can cause worry which in turn steals hope. We all have to make choices in life. It might be a basic choice, such as choosing whether we want to drink coffee or tea, to a more important decision, such as choosing which car to buy. The range of options we are faced with in the twenty-first century can be overwhelming. Technology has, in some ways, caused us a lot of problems with making decisions, because there are so many more options to choose from. Also, because we live in a very fast paced world, we often want to make instant decisions. It is okay to take time over making a decision, but not to the point where it costs you emotionally or takes too much time.

**Our lives are the sum total of
our choices and decisions**

Our decisions are extremely important as they shape and define us. We all want freedom of choice but actually if we have too much freedom, it can become a nightmare. Take a restaurant for example:

Mel and Jo go to a restaurant in town. There are 3 dishes on the menu. Lasagne, Cottage pie, and Steak. The steak is too expensive. How long and how difficult is it for them to choose which meal to eat? Probably fairly easy. Bob and Lana go to a restaurant in town. There are 57 dishes on the menu and they can afford any of them. How long and difficult is it for them to choose which meals to eat? It's probably a nightmare. It is also interesting to consider how likely Mel and Jo are to get food envy; angry for buying the wrong food. Probably not much at all – especially if they share. But for Bob and Lana food envy is much more likely.

If you take this analogy further – how difficult would it be to choose from a menu which only had one meal? Extremely easy.

The easiest way to choose something is to have very little choice.

See yourself as blessed. It is because we have so much choice that choosing becomes difficult.

The fear of making decisions can be so paralysing that we can procrastinate or fill up with anxiety. With hundreds of different toothpastes, university courses, and holidays to choose from decisions can become daunting.

What is the most effective way to choose something? It depends on the thing we are choosing. Some specific strategies are mentioned in the appendix.

Financial Decisions
If the choice is a financial one, the more expensive the product is, the more difficult a decision can become. For small purchases such as buying a book, remember that you can

always change your mind; you are not making a permanent decision:

**If you choose one book, the
other books will still be there.**

For something more expensive this may not be an option. In this case, how should we respond?

> Liam buys a car for £5000 but realises he doesn't like it. He feels as though he has wasted £5000. But he hasn't. Liam sells the car for £4000. He may have wasted the £1000 difference, but not £5000.

Notice Liam's shame and guilt was based on the <u>full</u> value of the car, "I've wasted £5000", not the difference, "I've wasted £1000". Often we tend to feel guilty or disappointed based on the <u>full</u> value and forget that we can resell something. This is also the case with fear.

> Susie is fearful about buying a similar car for £5000. She is scared that she will waste £5000 not £1000.

**Always take into consideration that
you can resell something.**

Rather than see the difference in price as a loss you can reword this as "experience money" or "hire charges". In this way, if you see making a bad decision as spending £1500 for an extended trial, rather than making an incorrect £5000 purchase, it will help reduce the fear of making a bad purchase. You cannot guarantee that the product will meet all your needs; there are no guarantees. Sometimes we have to take risks.

Risk to reward

Difference in Tastes

Remember that in decision-making we are all different. I may raise my eyebrows and think someone is being too pedantic when they spend five hours choosing a pair of shoes, but similarly the other person may think I am being overly fussy and procrastinating in making a decision when choosing what computer to purchase. Because we all have different priorities as to what is important, these differences will occur.

It is also worth bearing in mind the cost of not making a decision or getting stressed over a decision compared with the disappointment for making the wrong decision:

Is the stress I have for not making a decision greater than the stress, criticism or disappointment I might receive for making a wrong decision?

Subconscious differences

In making a film I am constantly bombarded with decisions that I would never have to think about in real life. Directors are faced with thousands of decisions. What colour cigarette case should the character have? What shade of colour should it be? Where should it be placed on the table? When there are financial decisions to make, the money can constrain the choice and decision-making. But with total freedom it can become a nightmare to choose.

Some people's response is "Well, nobody will notice". I do not always think this is an acceptable answer. Yes, some people may not _consciously_ notice. However, subtle differences can have an effect at a subconscious level. Consider the following:-

Jill goes into a hardware store to purchase fairy lights for her party. She is trying to choose whether to have the warm coloured white or the slightly blue tinted white. Her friend tells her "well, nobody will notice". When people arrive at the party, it is very unlikely that someone is going to say "I like the colour of your fairy lights". In other words, people will not necessarily notice the details but it may have an overall effect on people's mood. For example, someone at the party may say "It feels really cosy here, and I feel comfortable". Just because they don't consciously notice the difference between the warm and blue tinted lights does not mean that Jill's decision has not had an effect on the party goers. For this reason the response "Well nobody will notice" is not always a fitting response.

Decisions are not always final

With artistic decisions remember that you are not making a permanent decision (unless you paint watercolours). In most instances, you can come back and change something later. Sometimes it is easier to change something you don't like than to create something from scratch.

**It's often easier to correct a bad
decision than it is to make a decision.**

A lot about decision-making skills can be learnt from other crafts. How would a musician make a decision? How would a writer make a decision? How would an artist make a decision? When drawing a portrait, do you think an artist spends hours focusing on drawing the perfect nose? No – they simply block in rough shapes. As they progress, they will give increasing focus to the exact details they want. What's more, often they will not fear making a mistake, as they know that they can always make modifications later on.

**Our choices shape our future.
But even bad choices can be
turned around for good.**

**Don't let a bad decision define
you, learn something from it.**

171

Envy and Comparison

"Envy was one of the most potent causes of unhappiness." *Bertrand Russell*

Envy is defined in the Oxford English Dictionary as the "Desire to have a quality, possession, or other desirable thing belonging to someone else"[22]. Envy is similar to comparison, we compare our car to someone else's car and want one like theirs because theirs is better. We might see a friend who is particularly gifted at playing the cello and compare it to our own inferior or non-existent cello playing and subsequently envy their abilities.

Envy and comparison can contribute significantly to depression, especially when what we envy is seemingly beyond our reach. Why does envy steal hope? I believe envy steals hope because envy is deceptive. Envy embraces an unrealistic perspective of the world. It's like wanting a rose without its thorns. Someone may envy a talented pianist – but would they envy the years of practice; we don't tend to envy the complete package. In some examples the thorns are less obvious. For example, a boy is raised in a wealthy family. His father gives him a large lump sum to start his own business. We may envy him but is it the complete package? Have we missed the thorns?

Unfulfilled destiny fuels envy

Some teachers teach their pupils that there can be whoever they want to be. That they control their own destiny and fate. If they want to become a fireman, all they have to do is have enough training, passion and knowledge. Those children are effectively told that there is no chosen or predefined destiny, or fate to their lives; that they can totally control their own lives.

172

Can you choose where you were born? No. Your parents chose that. Can you choose your parents? No. Can you choose your upbringing and education? Little in the early stages of life. You cannot totally control your own life because you cannot choose these factors that predetermine your destiny in life.

My fate was not to be king of England. Even if I could try to relive my life again, no matter what I did, that would never come true. I was not meant to be king. The family I was born into pre-chose this for me. In contrast, I was chosen to be a boy. Even plastic surgery can't change DNA. So we do have pre-chosen destinies. I was not meant to be king. I was meant to be a boy. I might not like those predetermined callings but that doesn't change the fact they are predetermined.

If you were born as a peasant in 9ᵗʰ century England, you may only have had the choice of drinking water, milk or beer. That limited choice was predetermined by the place and time of your birth. Today choosing to drink orange or apple juice, may seemingly have nothing to do with destiny, and more to do with choice. We don't see it as destiny because we have an abundance of choice. My thoughts, however, are on the other end of the scale. I can choose to think pretty much anything. So where is the line between destiny and choice?

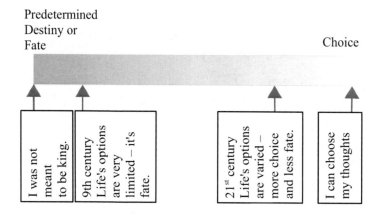

I believe there are often vaguer, pre-chosen – more subtle – destinies, based on the family I was born into, the town, the nature of my upbringing, social class, friends, connections etc.

Is career a destiny or a choice. In 9th century England it was pretty much a destiny; you didn't get much choice. But now we have more choice – though it is certainly limited. Books like "What colour is my parachute?" deal with this idea. If you have particular characteristics that run in your DNA, family, character, or society, you are going to be predisposed to do certain careers.

I was meant to be a musician. I wasn't meant to be a footballer. I cannot be whoever I just to be, I must walk the path of destiny. If I try to be something I am not called to be, I will live a life of frustration and disappointment.

Of course, other people have different destinies and this is where envy is so corrosive; it assumes that we can just become whoever we want to become. If my parachute is red, envying the career of someone who has a yellow parachute is futile.

Envy erodes hope because it compares destinies. It says "I'm not who I'm supposed to be". There are discrepancies between the following three identities and those create voids:

1. "Who I am **now**" - my identity as I see it now; most likely not fulfilling my destiny.

2. "Who I **want** to be" - this is looking at someone else and envying their identity and destiny.

3. "Who I **was meant to** be" - this is your pre-chosen destiny; what you were designed to do or what is in your genes.

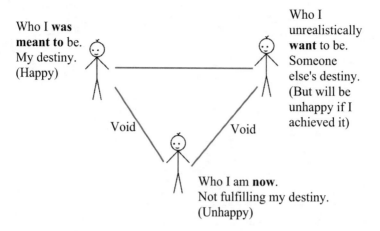

Who I **was** meant to be. My destiny. (Happy)

Who I unrealistically **want** to be. Someone else's destiny. (But will be unhappy if I achieved it)

Void

Void

Who I am **now**. Not fulfilling my destiny. (Unhappy)

Again, you may think that there is no such thing as a pre-chosen destiny, that "I am, and there is no other version of me." But that is not true. Let's look at a negative example. One thing is for certain – if you were born blind in the 1920s your destiny was almost *certainly not* to become a fighter pilot; you need 2020 vision for that. So if there is such a concept as "fate was against him", this clearly also works in a positive sense "destiny was on my side". If you are born in a musical family – it is *possible* that your destiny in life is to become a musician.

Perhaps you are still unconvinced in destiny. You may think "I am who I was meant to be". You may pretend you have no envy, pretend you are living your destiny. But if you think like this, you will never be fully satisfied as they are deceptions. Even if you try to ignore them, or even if you try to reason them away, envy of someone else's destiny and a sense of not fulfilling your destiny will always linger in the background as shadows.

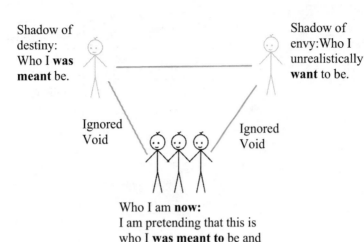

Shadow of destiny: Who I **was meant** be.

Shadow of envy: Who I unrealistically **want** to be.

Ignored Void

Ignored Void

Who I am **now:**
I am pretending that this is who I **was meant to** be and pretending that this is what I **want**.
(Fake happiness)

This concept may become clearer if we look at a real example of this. Pete has the gift of writing books – that is his destiny. He is excellent at it, but he has neglected it. He is now an accountant. He envies his friend who is a professional footballer. This can be represented as follows:

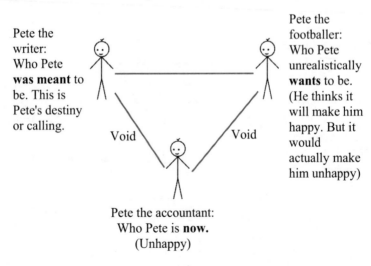

Pete the writer: Who Pete **was meant** to be. This is Pete's destiny or calling.

Pete the footballer: Who Pete unrealistically **wants** to be. (He thinks it will make him happy. But it would actually make him unhappy)

Void

Void

Pete the accountant: Who Pete is **now.** (Unhappy)

Pete feels unhappy. There are voids between who he is now, who he wants to, and who he was meant to be. He could try the self-deceptive method we mentioned above. He could tell himself "I always wanted to be an accountant, this is what I truly want for my life; I don't want to be a footballer or writer; I was meant to be an accountant, this is what I was born to do". However, thinking like this would be self-deception – the shadows would always linger. What Pete really needs to do is to become a writer.

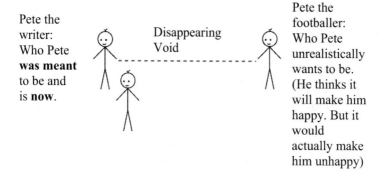

Pete the writer: Who Pete **was meant** to be and is **now**.

Disappearing Void

Pete the footballer: Who Pete unrealistically wants to be. (He thinks it will make him happy. But it would actually make him unhappy)

The key to avoiding envy is to believe that destiny exists and then discover your true individual destiny. This may take a while. As we explore and come to know ourselves, we will come to discover what our calling in life is. Subsequently, as we move towards our calling, envy will reduce.

Find your calling in life.
Who are you meant to be?

Envy makes assumptions

As seen in the previous chapters, one of the main issues of depression is how we use our memory and imagination. If we focus on what others have, we imagine having their ability, possession or attributes. Most likely we do this in an attempt to feel more accepted. However, we make some grave assumptions in the process.

Envy is impatient

If I envy someone's Ferrari I imagine having one right now i.e. "I want a Ferrari". We generally don't envy someone and think "Wow, he's got a Ferrari, I want one in ten years time". Envy is rooted in the present. The gap between reality and our imagination causes our emotions to spiral. Is it wrong to want a "Ferrari"? No, of course not. If we are quick to envy, we need to step back and consider life with a long-term perspective. Rather than seeing someone and thinking: "I want a Ferrari now", sit back and reflect on whether it is what you would really like, and then view it in terms of your lifespan. "I would like a Ferrari. I don't have one now. How can I achieve this goal within ten years time? Am I willing to put in the effort?". Note that even if you decided to be patient and save up for a Ferrari, that still might not bring happiness. Be careful envy can stem from impatience.

**Envy is based on the present
"I want it now"**

**Reconsider your desires within
the grand scheme of things.**

Envy is rooted in insecurity

Envy is often based on the three needs that we are all looking to fulfil: significance, security and acceptance. Why do we want a Ferrari? Why do we want to be like that other person? Is it simply that we are dissatisfied with ourselves, or that we feel insecure, insignificant or unaccepted? We refer to insecurity in the section on self-esteem (see page 245).

Envy is inward looking

Also, note that envy is closely linked to anger. We identified that anger can often result when we ruminate and obsess too long on what we want, rather than what others need. If we

178

spent less time focused on what we wanted, and focused out, we would have less potential to envy.

Ironically, three people can envy each other simultaneously. Can you see how sad this is?

Katy envies Evelyn for her beautiful looks.

Mimi envies Katy because she has lots of money.

Evelyn envies Mimi because she is extremely talented.

Comparison direction

Is comparison bad per se? No. Comparison can be used to inspire us to change. However, if we are going to compare, we need to compare objectively. Envy normally "compares up"; in other words, we generally compare ourselves with those we consider more fortunate, successful, rich, or talented than ourselves. Seldom do we compare down. If we compare down, we soon discover how fortunate we are. If we compare ourselves throughout history, that can also be enlightening. Compare ourselves with a king five-hundred years ago:

- We have more choice of food than a king did five hundred years ago.
- We can contact people quicker.
- We can travel quicker.
- We have more restaurants available.

179

- The quality and quantity of entertainment are substantially better.

- We generally have better health.

- We generally live longer.

- Our ease of living has greatly improved.

- The technology we have today is quite remarkable.

**In many ways you are richer than a
king was five hundred years ago**

**Aren't you so glad you are living today
and not five hundred years ago?**

Globalisation

Depression has increased radically in the recent decades; this puzzles scientists – especially given that there are more drugs, increasing research, and help is more readily available. Psychologists say that "the radical increase in depression is very hard to explain on biological grounds".[23] A lot of physical changes have taken place, such as the depletion of vitamins in our food, but no physical factor has changed to the exponential degree of the depression epidemic.

One suggestion is that more people are aware of depression and therefore more people are self-diagnosing and considering treatment. When the term depression was less well known, a lot of people may have suffered with depression but not realised it. This suggestion is more convincing, however, more than 50% of people suffering with depression still fail to approach their doctors.[24] I suggest an alternative view. Globalisation is one of the biggest things to have happened in recent years. Globalisation is good on many levels, however it comes with its problems.

One thousand years ago your world was your village. If there were two butchers in a village, and as a child you wanted to become a butcher, you'd either carry on the previous butcher's job or you would start your own. The competition would be the other two butchers and maybe some other classmates. The world was small and the competition was small. If you wanted to live in a big house – the definition of "big house" was defined by the biggest houses in that village. You may have envied, or set your goals on becoming the best butcher in town and living in a big house.

Fast forward to the twenty-first century. Now you are exposed to so much more. The biggest house is not the biggest house in the village, it's the biggest house in the world. No longer are you happy with becoming the best butcher in your village – but you want to be the best butcher in the world. With globalisation we are being exposed to more and more material goods, talents, skills, and ideas. As a result, there is more potential to envy others – and envy is a major contributor to depression.

Expectations to perform also seem to be rising. It is becoming increasingly more difficult to "meet the mark" in industries such as music, film, and sport. Increasing expectations may make people feel more under pressure.

Globalisation has also led to an abundance of choice. The more choice we have, the more potential we have for anger, frustration and confusion. Furthermore, today we are bombarded with negative news; we are probably exposed to more negative news in one month than in someone's lifetime a hundred years ago. Do we really need to know about serial rapists on the other side of the world, drought and wars etc? If we fill our memory banks with negative news, we are more likely to become depressed than hopeful. One example of the problem of globalisation is told in the following story:

In an African village some missionaries decided to install electricity and give the village access to TV. Previously the village had been fairly positive and happy. However, when the missionaries returned the year after, they found a village full of dissent and arguments, full of hatred and anger. Why? Because before they had seen TV they didn't really know how westerners lived, but after they had seen TV (the American with his Chevrolet, big house etc.) the villagers became jealous and envious. Their expectations soared to unrealistic levels and so did their levels of envy. That envy caused strife, depression and anger.

Earlier in the book we mentioned that you are more likely to suffer with depression if you live in a city. Obviously, there are other factors such as increased stress and noise pollution, but envy could also be a contributing factor to this statistic. Envy and thoughts of comparison can be triggered by where you live, your circumstances and lifestyle. Social media, such as Facebook, gives plenty of opportunities to start envying others. If you struggle with envy, avoiding Facebook may be a good decision.

**Facebook is an excellent place to become
envious and consequently depressed**

<u>Stop and consider</u>
As previously noted, will power is not necessarily the way to stop envying. It may be worth considering the following questions:

- What is the point in having fans on the other side of the world?

- Would it not be better to have ten strong friends in the street than a hundred shallow friends on the other side of the world?

- Can you not try to be satisfied with being special to a select group?

- Do you think books like "1000 places to see before you die" were written by one person? Do you think that it's possible to visit all those cities in a lifetime? Are you envying something that is unrealistic?

- Would it be better to live in one country and absorb the culture than try to visit every country in the world?

- What is better – quality or quantity?

- Are any friends envious of you?

- If everyone was the same, what would the world be like?

- Would you rather be a second-rate someone else or a first-rate you?

- Is genius about novelty or doing exceptionally well?

Fear, Worry and Anxiety

Fear and worry are great contributors to depression. If I told you that a bomb had been planted in your street and you believed me, you would fear or worry about it exploding. Your fear is based on your imagination. Remember, imagination functions by combining memories. Fear and worry will cause problems, regardless of whether the event is real or imagined. If I had been lying to you about the bomb, but you had believed it, you would still worry. So dealing with worry goes back to our search for truth and the way in which we recall and combine our memories.

Film directors often play on the idea of imagination. You would think that a gory monster would be the scariest thing to see in a film – it's not! The scariest monster in a film is the one which you don't see, where your imagination plays a large part. In the film Alien, for example, the scariest part is where you haven't seen the creature. Once the creature is revealed in the film, the fear level, in some respects, decreases.

**Your imagination can create
more fear than reality**

Worry

Worry is a fear that something might happen. Often what we play out in our thought-life is far worse than the reality. Perhaps you're running late to work due to a traffic delay. In your head you imagine arriving at work and your boss hitting the roof. What is your imagination based on – your memories of him doing that before? You may have discarded the memory that most Thursdays your boss is in a meeting and the chances of him noticing you are slim. (Please note: I am not an advocate of being late for work or making excuses).

There are many ways to deal with worry and I highly recommend the book "How to stop worrying and start living" by Dale Carnegie. One particular way to deal with your worries is to write them down and analyse them.

Write it down

Writing down your worries, your goals and your progress in life is a good way to combat depression. By writing down your worries, it allows you to put them aside and assess them from a more objective viewpoint. It also makes it easier to present these to someone else for advice. For example:

Jim gets home from work, he is very tired, he opens a letter telling him he needs to pay a large bill. He thinks "I don't know how I'm going to cope financially". He spends ages trying to think of how he is going to deal with it. He comes up with five ideas, which are rather muddled, but doesn't write them down, since being in such a negative mood, he sees only problems. He goes to bed exhausted. The next day he gets up and goes to work. On returning home tired, he sees the letter and starts panicking again. He tries to think of the five ideas he thought of yesterday, but can only remember two; he is now frustrated, not only about the letter, but also that he has forgotten his five ideas. His worries and stress have grown. He becomes more tired, more negative and falls into a negative spiral. It's very difficult to assess his thoughts rationally when he is in a ruminating state. His thoughts sound something like the following:

> "I don't know how I'm going to cope … I could try and take out a loan … I don't know how I'm going to cope … Oh no perhaps not a loan … perhaps I should … I don't know how I'm going to cope … maybe I should ask for a pay- rise … I don't know how I'm going to cope … I don't think they will give me a pay-rise … I don't know how I'm going to cope."

If Jim wrote down his worry "I don't know how I'm going to cope financially" on a piece of paper and thought "I'm tired – I need to be fresh to deal with this", he would avoid getting into a negative spiral of increasingly worried thoughts and tiredness. He could sit down the next morning – when he is fresher – and think of five different ways to combat this problem. If he comes back to them the next day, he can review his five combat methods without spending huge amounts of effort trying to recall what his ideas were.

When we write down and analyse our thoughts we can sometimes see how irrational they are. In doing so, one of the most useful questions we can ask ourselves is:

What is the worst that can happen?

Fear

Worry and fear are similar. Fear is an emotion that infiltrates every area of our lives. In fact, a lot of the other emotions and problems in this book could have a root emotion of fear.

Emotion/Problem	Root Fears
Guilt	The fear of someone finding out. The fear of our past impacting our future. The fear that we have damaged our sense of identity.
Worry	The fear of something bad happening.
Anxiety	Fear with an unidentified object
Scepticism	The fear of making a mistake. The fear of trusting.
Unforgiveness	The fear of lack of justice.
Perfectionism	The fear of not being significant. The fear of not being accepted.
Control Seeking	The fear of losing control. The fear of lack of justice.
Procrastination	The fear of not using time wisely. The fear of making a bad decision. The fear that making a bad decision will affect our significance, acceptance and security.
Isolation	The fear of thinking we won't fit it. The fear of what others think of us.
Workaholism	The fear of not making the most of time. The fear of examining ourselves. The fear of silence.

Envy	The fear that we are missing out.
Nostalgia	The fear that things won't get better. The fear of growing old.
Anger	The fear of losing control.
Singleness	The fear of being alone.
Disappointment	The fear that we missed out on the best.
Low self-esteem	The fear that I am and will continue to be insignificant and unaccepted.
Greed	The fear that if I don't have enough money I won't be able to cope. The fear that we are missing out.
Hoarding	The fear that I must keep something or that I won't have enough.

These fears are just the tip of the iceberg. Fears come in all shapes and sizes. People have fears of spiders, planes, clowns, small spaces, germs, dogs, crowds, heights, snakes, flying etc. The list is endless.

Healing fear

We have already seen that fears will cause problems, regardless of whether the event is real or imagined, rational or irrational. A spider in a room might definitely be there and not simply imagined. In the UK spiders are not poisonous, run at less than 2 mph, will not bite you, and are totally harmless, yet huge amounts of people have a phobia of them. Even if something is real in terms of being present, our imagination still fills in the details as to what they might do. Imagination is based on projecting our memories into the future, so in order to heal fears, it might be that healing our memories is the key.

Firstly, the way we talk about fears is unhelpful. We tend to see fears as something we own. We may say something like "I have a decidophobia (fear of making decisions)". If we learn to disown our fears, we can then see them more objectively. Simply changing how we talk about them may help them to subside. I can say "I sometimes experience fear when making a decision" rather than "I have decidophobia".

Secondly, we tend to see phobias in black or white terms. Either we have decidophobia or we don't. In reality, it is more of a sliding scale. Everyone will fear making a decision at least once in their life. Try to see fears more objectively.

In an earlier chapter I discussed replacement theory. We don't try to rid ourselves of depression by trying to remove it, but by instilling the opposite, by instilling hope. This works most effectively because it echoes how our memories work. Like depression, fear is based on negative memories. We must replace fear with courage, faith, trust, hope and love.

**Fear is based on our imaginations
and therefore memories.**

**The best way to get rid of fear
is to instil the opposite.**

Replace fear with courage and love

The first thing you could try is to list your fear and then try to think of the reasons why you may love the same thing. For example:

I ~~fear~~ making decisions

I love making decisions because...

1. If I never had any decisions, life would be dull.

2. Decisions show I have the freedom to choose.

3. If I have a lot of choice, it shows that I am blessed.

4. If we all made the same decisions, we would not be unique – the more decisions I make the more unique I will be.

5. Why would I want to copy everyone else's decisions all the time?

A lot of phobias stem from childhood. They were originally protection mechanisms that in time have become excessive. For example, "don't go near the fire" was screamed by a parent in order to protect a child. But when the child grew up they became extremely fearful of candles. The more traumatic experiences tend to create a stronger protection mechanism. As we grow older these mechanisms are no longer needed – or at least they are needed to a lesser degree. Sometimes these fears compound over time as memories making things even worse. Fears are stored as memories and can get stronger.

Returning to decidophobia. As a child, I probably made some bad decisions, or saw others making bad decisions, and, as a result, I became fearful of making decisions in order to protect myself. But now I do not need to keep these fears. These negative memories that protected me as a child now hinder me.

In order to heal our fears we need to heal our memories

Act despite the feelings
Fear is a feeling as well as a memory. It can take time to heal a memory. But in order to do so sometimes we have to ignore our feelings. We can feel the fear and act despite the feeling. As Susan Jeffers phrases it: "Feel the fear and do it anyway".

There are many speakers who claim they still have huge fear and anxiety before standing up and giving speeches. But they know that if they let those fears rule them, they will never do what they need to do. If you have a good imagination, I'm sure you could come up with potential fears for almost every situation. Fear of putting your feet on the floor in the morning: "You might have dropped a pin on the floor". There will always be a reason to fear, and if you focus on those fears you will end up emotionally paralysed.

There will always be a reason to fear,
and if you focus on those fears you
will end up emotionally paralysed.

The truth is that many of your fears will not come true. Statistics show that 90% of fears and worries never come true. Yes, worry and fears are "real", but these statistics show that fears are not necessarily "realistic". It is more realistic to be positive than negative. So act against your fears.

Everything you've ever wanted
is on the other side of fear.

You can handle it
What if your fears did come true? What if you feared redundancy and it actually happened? The underlying fear here is that somehow you wouldn't be able to handle it. If you knew you had the ability to handle any situation, you would have very little to fear. Have you ever lost a job? Did you handle it? Have you ever been sick? Did you handle it? I'm sure you have much more ability to handle situations than you realise.

Have you handled it before?
Has anyone else handled it?
You can handle more than you realise.

Guess what? If you never took any risks, you would never have anything to fear. To fear shows that you are trying; it shows that you have expectations and courage; it shows that you are growing. Also, remember that you are not alone. Many of the fears you have kept silent about are exactly the same fears others experience.

Disappointment

We all face disappointment in life but most people overcome it fairly quickly. If you focus on the event that has disappointed you for a long time, it can turn to rumination and depression. Firstly, recognise that disappointment is normal. Everyone faces it. Secondly, we often see disappointment in a negative light. Can you imagine a life in which your will was never crossed and everything happened exactly your way; what kind of person would that make you?

Disappointment versus Relief
On the day the Titanic took sail Thomas Hart had his papers stolen and therefore couldn't board the once in a lifetime voyage. After this setback he was so disappointed that he roamed around Southampton, too ashamed to go home and admit to his relatives he had missed the voyage. I'm sure when he found out that the Titanic had sunk his disappointment soon turned to relief.

Hindsight is a wonderful thing. Disappointment is always rooted in the present and we often fail to see what further disappointments or problems may be down the line. One small disappointment might prevent us from having a greater disappointment or problem. Of course, in the incident of the Titanic, we find out the full story. We have hindsight on our side. However, we might not. Let's look at another example.

Hank was handsome and extremely sought after by the girls. When Helen married him Debbie and Rachel were really disappointed. Several years later Debbie moved away to another area and lost contact with Hank. Rachel, however, stayed in the area. After another five years Helen left Hank. Helen told Rachel how her marriage had been a tough time, that Hank was abusive, often got drunk and hit her. Rachel was relieved that she had never married Hank. However, Debbie didn't hear about the marriage breakdown. She spent the rest of her life in despair, sad that she had never been able to marry Hank. Rachel's hindsight allowed her to experience relief. In contrast, Debbie had a lack of hindsight; she was disappointed about something that she should actually have been thankful for.

Because we never see the full picture of life, it is impossible to see which disappointments we have experienced have actually saved us from something worse. It is hard to know. Even something like someone turning up late to a party might have prevented them from being in a road accident.

It may be disappointment now, but it might be a relief in hindsight. Your disappointment might have saved you from something worse.

Disappointment can be prevention.

Expectations
In order to deal with disappointment people sometimes say "Don't get your hopes up", "Don't set your standards too high, because you'll be disappointed". Let's take this further. Why not say: "The best way to avoid disappointment is never to get your hopes up, never to aim at anything, never set to any goals."

If you aim at nothing in life, you'll hit every time. However, is it not better to aim at the sun and hit the moon, than aim at nothing and hit every time?

"Aim for the sun...when you hit the moon, rejoice...you've finally succeeded in graduating from the delusion of mediocrity." *John Nolan*

**"You are not going to succeed in everything you attempt in life. That's guaranteed.
In fact, the more you do in life,
the more chance there is *not*
to succeed in some things."**[25]

<u>See the gold amongst the rubbish</u>
Nobody wants to live a mediocre life. Disappointment is also about seeing what you have achieved despite a "so-called failure." We should ask ourselves a variety of questions after a disappointment. Some areas which you may want to consider are as follows:

- How has this setback benefited me emotionally?
- What have I learnt despite this setback?
- How have I benefited financially? For example, if you couldn't go with your friends to a stag party you may have saved a lot of money as a result.
- How has this disappointment benefited my skill set?
- How has this disappointment enriched my life?
- How has this setback led me to explore new areas and skills in life?
- How has this disappointment made me more resilient?
- What has this setback prevented me from experiencing?
- Did it actually cause any harm at all?

One personal example of disappointment has been to do with my career. When I was at university I always thought I wanted to be a film composer. On coming out of university I tried various ways to get into the industry but it was exceptionally difficult. If you put 1000 grains of sand into a funnel and momentarily undo the bottom, only a few of these will succeed in getting through. Each grain of sand may be fighting just as hard as the others but they don't get through. The myth is, "The harder you market yourself, the more you will succeed". Not necessarily. I know some extremely bright and determined people who have failed to enter that industry, and some easy going people of average ability who seem to land on their feet all the time. For those who have relatives or contacts in the industry, it is like cutting butter with a hot knife. They've never known how difficult it is for outsiders to break in, simply by having a lot of finances and influences behind them, they have taken a lot for granted.

Despite my disappointments at breaking into the industry I ended up working in teaching English as a foreign language, working in a camera shop, being a wedding photographer, working in pensions software, and turning my hand to film making. If I'd gone straight from university to writing film music, I would have missed out on all those other enriching experiences. I could have ended up on a conveyor belt of life simply churning out soundtrack after soundtrack. If I'd gone into film music I certainly wouldn't have made or scored my own film. It certainly is more rewarding scoring music to a film that you've made yourself, than scoring for someone else's film.

Sometimes people who reach their goals early in life have nowhere to aim at. Sometimes they get stuck on a conveyor belt and they have little time to develop and hone their skills. They are simply too busy churning out work to stop and learn new things. Furthermore, people who often reach goals very quickly take their luck and privileges for granted. If a composer has a multimillionaire background and the first piece he writes is played by a top London orchestra, he could be considered to be very successful in a short amount of time. Most composers would not achieve that level of success in such a short period of time. The privileged composer could end up thinking his success was normal, and fail to realise how privileged he was. He could make statements to other composers such as "Why don't you just record your music with the London Symphony Orchestra?", taking for granted his fortunate financial background. In contrast, if you've waited half your life to have something played by a live orchestra and then it happens, you are less likely to take things for granted.

Of course, not all disappointment, is prevention or can be seen as sending us in a different direction. Sometimes it is much harder to see the benefits. For example, if you break a leg tripping over something and you are disappointed with yourself for not looking where you were going, you need to deal with that kind of disappointment. Disappointments are similar to anger, so we should be quick to resolve it. We also need to learn how to practise forgiving ourselves and others.

Scepticism rather than Trust

Scepticism, hesitation, cynicism, and reasoning can all hinder trust. Some of us find it difficult to trust, but we all need to. I've never been to the Antarctic but I trusted my teacher at school when she told me that penguins were there. I don't question that prices are correctly labelled in the supermarket, that the person who made me coffee used a clean cup. When I sit down on a chair I never question whether it has any defects. If I did try to investigate every single aspect of these things, not only would I waste a lot of time and wear myself out, but I would also end up paralysed by the lack of trust.

If we question everything, we'll end up being emotionally paralysed and waste a lot of time. Sometimes we have to trust.

Of course, this doesn't mean simply trusting to the point where we put ourselves in foolish situations, but if I spend my life paralysed by cynicism, that may be actually a worse outcome than if I'd trusted and made a mistake.

Trusting Trudy and Sceptical Shelley both own large mansions in the countryside. They need help to run the mansion and with the accounts. Trudy employs a young person to take care of these tasks. She has a trusting attitude. After five years Trudy finds that her employee has not only stolen a few small trinkets but has also siphoned off a couple of thousand pounds from the accounts. Shelley, on the other hand, is so scared that someone might steal from her that she spends a year procrastinating and doing all the work herself, and then, when she employs someone, she is constantly following them around and checking on them; she is constantly paranoid and doesn't sleep at night. Nobody likes to have things stolen from them but who out of these had the worst deal?

Trusting Trudy
> Emotional Benefits:
>> • No pain of procrastination.
>> • Lack of worry and fear until she found out that the employee had stolen from her.
> Physical Benefits:
>> • The first year she didn't have to do all the work herself, she could sleep at night.
> Emotional Costs:
>> • Some short-lived disappointment at losing £2000 and some trinkets.
> Physical Costs:
>> • £2000 and some trinkets.

196

Sceptical Shelley

    Emotional Benefits:

- None

    Physical Benefits:

- She minimised the likelihood of money being stolen.

    Emotional Costs:

- The pain of procrastination.
- Worry

    Physical Costs:

- She had to do all the work herself for the first year.
- Tired all the time.

I would say that Shelley actually paid more. The cost to her emotions was much greater than what Trudy lost in finances. Sometimes we have to consider the emotional cost more than the potential problem resulting from trusting.

Scepticism could cost you more emotionally than the cost you might pay for mistrusting

Often we think that understanding is key to trusting. If only we could understand something or somebody, then we would be able to trust more. This is sometimes true, however, you don't always have to understand in order to trust. For instance, I don't have to understand how a train works in order to take a journey on one. Besides, even if you do understand a lot about something/someone, that understanding doesn't necessarily lead to trust. For example, if I knew everything about a train, including the dangers and potential faults, that might actually hinder trust. You will often find that trust leads to understanding.

Don't wait to understand in order to trust.

Relationships and trust

Relationships are based on trust. One of the reasons that so many people are single or lonely is that they find it hard to trust others. Sadly, because of a lot of bad stories in the news, people end up with a high degree of scepticism. Perhaps you read a story of someone dating a serial murderer. What are the odds this will happen to you? Are you sceptical because you are focusing on negative news and negative experiences? Are you tarring everyone with the same brush? Consider the following:

Sandra has been through many relationships. Every boyfriend has cheated on her within the first two months. Now Sandra turns down every offer of a date. She is scared that it might happen again. Can she ever trust a man again? She has three options:

1. Never date again and risk becoming isolated, lonely and cold-hearted.

2. Try dating again but question and doubt everything. Try to figure out whether it will work. Analyse every move by the man in detail. Be sceptical and cynical. And pretty much guarantee becoming paranoid and anxious.

3. Learn to trust again. Risk being hurt, but also risk finding the man of her dreams.

There are relationships that work!! If Sandra has to go through another three painful experiences to then meet the dream guy on her fourth date, can she see the pain as part of the learning curve? Let's say it takes Sandra two months of pain to get over each man, in total that would be six months of pain. Would six months of heartache be worth paying in order to have 20, 30, 40+ years of fulfilling marriage afterwards? Rather than seeing suffering for suffering's sake – can she see it as a sacrifice – a way of learning? Besides, where has she met all these men? Can she try a different approach? If she met all these men on a particular internet site, perhaps she needs to change tactics; try to meet someone at a dance class, church group, different town, be more verbal about her emotions etc.

Suffering

Is trust the issue or is it how we perceive suffering? Lack of trust doesn't guarantee us a lack of suffering. Lack of trust only leads us to a place where there is no possibility of healing. To explain this I shall use a picture:

> Find me a dark bank vault deep underground.
> Take out my heart.
> Lock it in a box.
> Put it in a safe and throw away the key.
> Let nobody touch my heart.
> Let it stay cold in that safe for a million years, until the blood dries up and it goes hard. Then I can be lifeless, loveless, knowing no joy or emotion.
> Then the pain will come from within rather than risking the external pain from the world of life up above.
>
> Life up above?!
>
> No.
> My heart has been in this box too long.
> Come and unlock my heart.
> I want to be free to love.
> Free to feel blood pump through my veins.
> I want to come back to the surface, where rippling streams dance in the light of the day.
> Yes, my heart may be hurt up here, where butterflies and birds fly on the breeze.
> But if I'm hurt up here externally, at least it's a

place where healing can come and I can enjoy life again.

It's better to be vulnerable in the healing warmth of the sun,
Than to feel pain in the depths of coldness where there will never be any doctor or physician who can heal my heart.
Help me to hope.
Help me to trust.
Help me to love again.

When we trust we make ourselves vulnerable. We open ourselves up to the possibility of emotional pain. But we need to learn to trust. I repeat: "Lack of trust doesn't guarantee us a lack of suffering. Lack of trust only leads us to a place where there is no possibility of healing."

We need to trust others otherwise we end up emotionally paralysed.

<u>What and Who?</u>
The question is not whether we should trust. We have to. It's a question of what and who we should put our trust in.

Guilt
Guilt can crush us emotionally. Just like fear and worry, guilt can be based on incorrect facts. For example:

Dillon felt guilty. He'd told his friend that he would be at his birthday party on Friday night and bring along the birthday cake, but then his boss asked him to put in some extra hours at work. Dillon now feels guilty about not going to the party and for letting his friends down. However, the next day he finds out that the party was cancelled last minute due to his friend also needing to stay late at work. Dillon could have spent the night feeling guilty about not going, but that guilt was a feeling not based upon a fact.

Are you feeling guilty
based on incorrect facts?

Of course, not all guilt is based on incorrect facts. If you crash into the back of someone's car because you were texting at the wheel, that guilt is a result of something you've done wrong. Firstly, recognise that to feel momentarily bad is actually a good thing. Why? If you never felt guilty for doing something wrong, you'd never learn from your mistakes.

Wayne went into the supermarket and when something didn't scan properly at the self-checkout he put it in his bag anyway. He never thought twice that what he did was wrong. He continued this behaviour for years and it eventually led to more serious shoplifting. He felt no guilt or shame in what he was doing. When he landed up in prison for a serious crime, he still didn't feel guilty. "What have I done wrong?!" he exclaimed in court. Margaret, on the other hand, felt guilty the first time she slipped an item in her bag. Her feelings of guilt were so terrible that she didn't sleep that night. Did she ever slip an unpaid item into her bag again? No.

Momentary guilt is a warning signal telling us not to do it again. Guilt actually shows that you have morals and principles. Even prolonged guilt can sometimes be a warning signal. If someone leaves a shop with a TV without paying for it, they may feel guilty for weeks. Only when they return the TV to the shop and tell them that they had stolen it may the guilt subside. Guilt can often be based on the fear of being found out. Often the cost and consequences of owning up to making a mistake are smaller than the emotional cost of the guilt.

Confessing to what you've done may be the first step to destroying emotions of guilt and shame.

As we can see, guilt can be constructive – it warns us to stop. In this way, it is similar to a warning light on the dashboard of a car. The warning light will go out the sooner the problem is dealt with. Likewise, the sooner we fix the underlying issue, the sooner we will rid ourselves of guilt.

Shame

Guilt can become dangerous and destructive when it turns to shame. Normally guilt is about actions and shame is about identity. When we experience shame, we tend to draw negative conclusions about ourselves. For example, "I lied" is guilt. "Therefore, I am a liar" is shame. Note here the word "Therefore" is common. When guilt becomes shame we make false conclusions such as the following:

- I've stolen something, *therefore I am a bad person.*
- I missed the work deadline, *therefore I am useless.*
- I hurt her feelings, *therefore I'll never be able to find a wife, I'm unlovable.*

As seen in the section on lies, combining statements with a view about ourselves is a common cognitive trap. Just because you've missed a work deadline does not make you useless. Firstly, recognise that we all make mistakes in life. Mistakes are not failures in themselves, it is only a failure if we fail to learn from them.

Accepting compliments and gifts despite how we feel
Sometimes we can feel guilty about people being nice to us. Those suffering with depression may find it difficult to accept compliments and affirmation. During depression people often find it difficult to receive physical gifts, affection etc. They may use phrases such as "I don't deserve it", or can't see the

point; they may think the other person is lying or has ulterior motives. Consider the following:

**It's not what you deserve,
it's what you need.**

Do you really think your stomach _deserves_ food – what exactly has it contributed? Your stomach probably doesn't _deserve_ much in terms of moral, intellectual, or emotional contribution. It does, however, _need_ to be fed.

Shame and guilt can rob us of what we need, whether we deserve it or not. It can also rob the giver. If I bought a nice birthday present for one of my nephews and when I gave it to him he said "Sorry uncle Steve, I don't deserve it" what would my reaction be? It would hurt my feelings that he didn't want to receive the gift I'd bought him. When we are depressed we tend to think of being an inconvenience to others and that if they try to give us time, attention, affection or other objects, that they shouldn't. But when shame causes us to refuse their gifts, we are actually robbing the other person the joy of giving.

Shame can rob us of receiving. Also, by refusing to receive, we rob the giver of the joy of giving.

For us to reject someone's love is more of an inconvenience than to accept it. It costs the other person emotionally.

You are not an inconvenience.

**Guilt and shame are corrosive.
Open up to others about your
thoughts and feelings.**

Nostalgia and Regret

The Collins dictionary defines nostalgia as "a yearning for the return of past circumstances, events, etc."[26] Nostalgia can sometimes contribute to depression and can be deceptive. When we think about the past, we tend to forget the bad things and magnify the good. But in the present, we tend to magnify the problems and diminish the good. So our comparisons between the present and past are often skewed.

I remember going on holiday and being quite low during the holiday because I noticed all my problems and my loneliness. A few years later I told someone how it was such a lovely holiday. I'd remembered all the wonderful scenery and food but forgotten the problems I'd encountered.

You may wish to live your life as it was 10 years ago. However, if you could live a day from your life then, side-by-side with a day from your life now, I think you'd be remarkably surprised at the difference. Remember, your nostalgic thoughts are not always correct.

Magnify the good in the present

Nostalgia is not so much of an issue for a ten year old. But as we get older we have more memories of the past to draw upon. So it is much more likely that we fall into this trap of comparing the past with now. Instead of magnifying all the problems of now and magnifying all the good times of yesterday, try to magnify the good times of today. Also remember:

You're never too old to start something new

Self-punishment

We often think that by warning others or punishing them, we can solve problems. You may also be prone to self-punishment. However, this seldom works as seen in the following example.

> Gary is a borderline alcoholic. Laura tells Gary that if he continues drinking, she will stop being his friend. Laura also tells Gary that he is likely to develop liver problems. She shows him an article that alcoholics die earlier and that he should stop drinking. You may think the last thing that Gary would do is now go out and get drunk. You may think that Gary would be worried about losing his friend, worried about damaging his liver, and that he would stop drinking. However, after Laura said this, Gary went out and drank more alcohol than he ever drank before.

Laura may have thought she was helping Gary by warning and threatening him. The fear of losing Laura as a friend, may have crossed Gary's mind, but this kind of threat seldom works. Punishments and warnings are not always the most effective way to help someone. What this did was make Gary feel guilty about his drinking. He felt shameful about himself. It made him feel useless and magnified his insecurities. The drinking in itself was the unhelpful coping mechanism for these identity issues and therefore he ended up turning to the bottle as a result of what Laura said.

Warning and punishment are not good ways to motivate people because they tend to send people into a spiral of shame. Behaviour is often linked to someone's identity, so by targeting behaviour, people feel as though their identity is being attacked. On the whole, rather than _punishing bad behaviour_, we are better _rewarding good behaviour_. Better still, focus on *building good character*. Instilling truth and hope is a much more effective way of helping someone overcome their problems.

Self-Pity

Self-pity can be a major cause of depression. The word *"self-pity"* is a rather strange one. We normally use the word pity like sympathy or compassion. "I saw a stranger and had pity on them; I sympathised with them and showed them some love and compassion". On the contrary, *self-pity* is not showing love and compassion to yourself, it's feeling sorry for yourself.

> "Feeling sorry for yourself and your present condition, is not only a waste of energy but the worst habit you could possibly have."
> *Dale Carnegie*

> "Self-pity is a losing strategy. It repels others and weakens you." *Michael Josephson*

Self-Pity is a damaging emotion. But why do we do it? I believe that the majority of self-pity is pre-rehearsed attention seeking.

Self-Pity is Pre-rehearsed Attention Seeking
"Self-pity" is closely linked with "Attention seeking". "Attention seeking" is effectively "other-pity". We can see the link between self-pity and attention seeking by looking at the language used. For example:

> Jenny's car has broken down. She says to herself: "Oh! My life is *always* going wrong. This car is *utterly* useless". Later on Jenny meets Paul. "Oh Paul! My life is *always* going wrong. My car is *utterly* useless".

206

Jenny may not be intentionally seeking attention or looking for pity from Paul, but subconsciously she is. Self-pity and attention seeking use exactly the same word formation and formed in the same part of the brain. Both stem from the inability to accept oneself. Self-pity and attention seeking both scream out: "I long for acceptance".

When we give a speech in public, we may recite things over and over again. If we are going to a business meeting, we may pre-hearse answers. Why? It's not for our sake. It's for the sake of gaining the other person's attention. For example:

Kevin is going to an interview. He keeps saying to himself "My aim in this business is to be a great team player, to develop better computer systems". Why is he rehearsing this? For himself? No. He is pre-rehearsing so that when the question comes he can gain the acceptance of the company.

In order to understand self-pity and feeling unaccepted we need to look at its source.

<u>The source of self-pity</u>
Self-pity can be a survival technique. The person who begs the hardest, wins the bread. For example:

> During a famine two women walk 20 miles to the king. The first says she is tired and her 7 children are in need of food. The second woman says she's *totally* exhausted, and her 7 children are *dying*. Who will the king have pity on?

In the west, this kind of self-pity is more evident in the survival techniques of children. A child will exaggerate when they want food: "Mummy, I'm starving, I'm really hungry" Are they? No, they are just trying to get sympathy to gain more food. In this way, *self-pity* and *attention seeking* may be partly a survival technique but when someone has turned to anorexia, cutting themselves, constantly beating themselves up emotionally, or looking for sympathy in every situation it becomes debilitating and will steal hope.

Even though self-pity has been used for centuries as a survival technique, note it is still rooted in the fear of rejection. The women who has "dying" children fears the rejection of the king.

The majority of self-pity stems from feelings of rejection. Consider the following:

> Joe is seven years old and lonely. At school he sits in the corner of the playground on a small wall and plays cards with himself. The rest of his class never seem to notice him or want to play with him; it is as though he were invisible. One day whilst running across the playground, he trips up and grazes his knee. All the pretty girls rush over to him and check to see if he is alright. "Joe, can I get you a plaster?" The girls nurse and show him attention. Months later Joe goes on a school trip. He sits at the back of the bus and none of the other children talk to him. During the outing Joe breaks a leg. For the next few weeks Joe has to be pushed round in a wheelchair. All the children want to take turns at pushing the wheelchair. The children suddenly show an interest in him.

Joe likes the attention he receives when he is ill. It makes him feel good. He starts to become addicted to this kind of attention. In the subconscious brain Joe is learning the following beliefs:

Negative belief: If I have problems people will show me attention.

Negative belief: If I don't have problems people will ignore me.

In Joe's instance his physical problems attracted the acceptance of others. On a conscious level Joe does not want to be physically ill. However, his subconscious brain may want to hold onto his physical ailments as it sees them as a useful means of gaining acceptance.

This phenomenon, of our subconscious brains wanting to hang onto problems as a means of acceptance, also applies to mental health issues.

Consciously most of us think that mental health issues are bad. Most of us want to get rid of depression. However, if you've constantly received attention when you've had problems, you may actually subconsciously desire those problems – because those problems make you feel accepted. Part of your brain may want to hold onto depression, anxiety or mental health problems.

On a subconscious level our brains may want to hang onto problems in order to gain acceptance and empathy.

Compounding Effect

Attention seeking and self-pity can become worse when they backfire. When we search for pity and don't receive it, these emotions can become stronger. For example, if you have a broken arm and people fail to notice, you may exaggerate the pain even more. If people still fail to notice, your subconscious may look for bigger problems to use as emotional leverage. The negative belief is as follows:

"If I have problems people will notice me. They didn't notice my broken arm, so I need a bigger problem to gain their acceptance."

Identity
Because self-pity is rooted in the inability to accept oneself, it is important to briefly look at identity.

Who are you? What is your identity? A person's sense of identity is often founded on one of the following:

- My identity is based on my work and career. If I lose my career, I will lose my identity.
- My identity is based on my education and knowledge.
- My identity is based on relationship.
- My identity is based on belonging to a group.
- My identity is based on my sexuality.
- My identity is based on my illness. If I wasn't ill I don't know who I'd be.

It is possible that people make an illness their identity. This is unhealthy. I once witnessed two anxiety sufferers high-five each other when they found out they had the same issues. What did this mean? Did this mean that their identity was based upon their diagnosis? What if they didn't have anxiety, who would they be?

We mentioned that we can subconsciously hang onto problems because they are useful to gain acceptance. Likewise, it might be that we subconsciously hang onto an illness, because we don't know who we'd be without it.

Do you want to get better?
Yes consciously you might.
However, do you subconsciously want to
hang on to depression because it gives you
some sense of acceptance and identity.

Who would you be if you
weren't depressed?

Healing Self-Pity
So how do we overcome self-pity? Firstly, we need to realise that having, holding onto, or even inviting problems is not the best way to find acceptance. If we take self-pity to an extreme, we can see how silly it is.

> Stephen is going to a party at the weekend. He finds he is never the centre of attention; he feels he is always in the background. Stephen decides to give himself a black-eye so that people notice him.

Surely there are much more effective ways to gain acceptance? How about gaining the acceptance of others by praising them or being thankful – that is a very attractive trait.

Having problems is not the best way
to get people to accept and notice you,
there are much more effective ways.

Secondly, realise that not everyone is going to accept you; it is better to have 12 good friends than 1000 shallow ones. Studies suggest that humans can really only maintain five close friends.[27]

Thirdly, and most importantly, we need to start building self-esteem. We need to focus on self-acceptance. If you can accept yourself, then you're not going to be constantly looking for the acceptance of others. Part of self-acceptance is dealing with our negative beliefs by replacing them with positive beliefs. Start telling yourself:

I don't need acceptance based on my problems, it's artificial.

I want people to accept me based on my good attributes.

Start noticing the people who do accept you and thanking them.

To overcome self-pity we need to heal our memories and start replacing them with new ones. We are not going to get rid of self-pity by trying to dig it out, we need to replace it by pouring in the antidote. Forgiving those who have hurt us, and forgiving ourselves is likely to be part of the process. In Joe's case, he needs to forgive his classmates at school for only showing him attention whilst ill. It is to forgiveness that we now turn.

Bitterness rather than Forgiveness

Bitterness: "Anger and disappointment at being treated unfairly; resentment."[28]

Forgiveness: "To stop blaming or being angry with someone for something that person has done, or not punish them for something"[29]

Lacking forgiveness and harbouring bitterness towards others can steal our joy and hope. By withholding forgiveness you cannot change the other person. Withholding forgiveness only harms oneself. For example:

Richard is a loyal man. Recently, his partner Katy left him and has been travelling around the world with another man. Richard didn't deserve this. It may be tempting for Richard to feel bitter towards Katy. However, what good does this achieve? If Katy is enjoying herself travelling on the other side of the world, Richard's bitterness won't affect her – it will only affect him. By remaining bitter towards someone we allow them to continue harming us. Forgiveness is <u>not</u> easy but it is necessary for our own sake.

So how do we genuinely forgive? Firstly, realise that forgiveness is a choice and that your feelings take time to catch up with your actions. Secondly, try to identify the real source of the problem. For example:

You are waiting for a coffee and a man barges into the queue and then gets angry and aggressive because his coffee is not fully topped up. Whilst this is not acceptable behaviour, what we might not see is that his wife had walked out on him that morning, or that he had just lost his job. We don't always get the full picture, and when we do, it can make us more compassionate and understanding.

We also need to realise that we ourselves are not perfect, we all make mistakes, and all need forgiving by others. Let's not be hypocrites. It's very easy to start being critical of say, drug abusers and alcoholics, but we all have addictions to a certain extent: addictions to coffee, to eating, to watching TV, to being arrogant, stubborn etc.

Did you choose which family you were born into? If you'd been born into a family where stealing was the norm and encouraged by the parents - how would you have turned out? It's easy to be judgemental towards someone and forget the blessing of being born into your family. Besides, did this happen overnight?

213

Most of us are similar to proverbial frogs in water. If a frog is thrown into hot water, it will jump out. If it is put in cold water and heated, it will slowly die. Nobody woke up one morning and thought "I know I think I will become a murderer". They slipped into it by a series of small bad choices. If you were in their shoes, could it have happened to you?

Avoid bitter triggers
In order to forgive, sometimes we need to avoid the triggers that set off unforgiving thoughts. Fred regularly parks his car next to the local bakery and walks to work. One day he returns to his car to find it is badly scratched. Every morning he parks in the same space and his head is full of angry thoughts towards the unidentified person who did this. The space is a negative trigger reminding him of what happened. Eventually, Fred decides to find a new parking space, a couple of roads away near the local park. Having removed the association he is much more able to forget and consequently forgive what has happened.

Some discretion is needed here. Sometimes the trigger could be a person. It can sometimes be impossible to avoid people, especially if you work with them. And at times it might be better to work through the issue than avoid the issue. If every-time you avoid something that triggers bitterness, you could end up avoiding the whole world. A balance must be found between the following two statements:

"Avoid triggers that allow bitter thoughts to rise"

"If you avoid every trigger that allows bitter thoughts to rise, you may end up isolating yourself."

<u>Replace bitter triggers</u>

Avoidance is not always the best option. Avoidance may be part of the forgiveness process but it isn't true forgiveness. True forgiveness is about creating new positive memory associations. Ideally, we want to turn negative triggers into positive triggers. Consider the following:

Gavin stole money from me. The name "Gavin" is a negative trigger that fills me with bitter feelings every time it is mentioned. Even if it is not the Gavin I am referring to, the name still cripples me. A different Gavin on the TV is mentioned; immediately I can feel bitterness rise inside me. I can avoid mentioning or listening to the name "Gavin" and this may temporarily help. However, if I truly forgive "Gavin" and do something good for him, such as take him a present, I will create a new memory association whereby the word "Gavin" will trigger positive memories. Now the word "Gavin" can be mentioned in passing on the TV and I no longer have to suffer bitterness and shame. A tough thing to do, but it explains the wisdom of Solomon:

> "If your enemy is hungry, give him food to eat; if
> he is thirsty, give him water to drink. In doing this,
> you will heap burning coals on his head."[30]

It's not about letting them off the hook. It's about healing our memories. To be able to hear the name "Gavin" again without feeling bitter – that is a great reward. Of course, a present is not the only way to create a new positive memory association. Get creative and think outside the box.

**True forgiveness is about creating
new positive memory associations.**

As we learn to forgive, hope will flow.

People are more forgiving than we realise

We can find hope by forgiving others. Also, ideally we should try to place ourselves in an environment of forgiveness. We can find hope by surrounding ourselves with forgiving people and believing that people are generally more forgiving than we realise.

George is looking after his mother's house while she is away on holiday. Whilst he is there he accidentally knocks a beautiful vase which crashes to the floor. If he believes that his mother is unforgiving he'll be full of fear and torment. If he believes that his mother will be forgiving, then he will not be full of fear and worry. Note that it is his belief that affects his emotions, not the reality. For example, if George believes that his mother is unforgiving, despite his mother being a very forgiving person, he will still be full of worry and fear.

Self-forgiveness

Self-forgiveness can be one of the hardest things to practise. Sometimes it is very difficult to forgive ourselves for something we have done. However, the same principles apply to general forgiveness.

Stop and consider

In forgiving somebody you may want to consider the following questions:

- What do *you* know now that *you* didn't back then? How can you beat yourself up about something you didn't know?

- What do *they* know now that *they* didn't back then? How can you harbour anger against them for something they didn't know?

- What exactly do you want to achieve?

- What are the emotional costs of what you want to

216

achieve?

- If I were in a similar situation to them, what would I have done?

- If someone else were in a similar situation to you, what would they have done?

- How did the other person fall into that trap? Could I have fallen into the same trap?

- What was the source of the other person's problem?

- Do you think the other person chose to become who they are overnight?

- How can I turn a negative trigger into a positive trigger?

Thankfulness

Practising thankfulness is a good way to dissipate anxiety and depression. However, sometimes it can be a real struggle to think of things to be happy about when you are tired and depressed because you are so busy ruminating about negative things. Community is important; to find friends to remind you of what you can be thankful for. You can ask your friends what special, unique or nice attributes you have. It is a good idea to write them down, so that you have something to come back to when you are struggling with negative thoughts. Also, don't forget that being thankful for what you have goes beyond the material world. We live in such a materialistic world that it is easy to forget the other aspects of life.

"Gratitude makes sense of our past, brings peace for today, and creates a vision for tomorrow."
Melody Beattie

Thankfulness generates hope.

Aspects of life	Examples of things to be thankful for
Character	I am patient with people. I am polite.
Abilities	I can use a computer. I can read. I can bake a cake.
Family and Friends	I have nephews and nieces. My parents love me.
Material Possessions	I own a piano. I have a bed. I have a phone.
Body / Looks / Physical Health	I am tall. I have blue eyes. I can run.
Home	I have a roof over my head. I have running water. I live in the Cotswolds.
Money	I can afford to buy a sandwich.
Work	I have a job.
Sport	I can swim. I can ride a bike. I have a bike.
Partner/Sex	At least I don't have any STDs

**Every day presents an opportunity
to add something to your list.**

Thankfulness, just like truth, is like a shield. If we build fast reflexes, we can stop the arrows of negativity getting to us. Don't let the arrows wound you first; practise thankfulness until your reflex actions are fast.

> **"If you start by being thankful for
> small things, you will soon have
> big things to be thankful for."**
> *Joyce Meyer*

Perfectionism

What is Perfectionism?

What exactly is perfectionism? The Cambridge dictionary defines a perfectionist as:

> "a person who wants *everything* to be perfect and demands the highest standards possible"[31]

Firstly, I don't agree with that definition because of the word everything. A surgeon might demand the highest standard possible on in the operating theatre but when it comes to keeping his garden trim might have much more relaxed standards. The Oxford dictionary states:

> "A person who refuses to accept *any* standard short of perfection"[32]

Again the word *any* throws us. We also have some problems because some things can be done perfectly, whilst others not. If I ask you what 2+2 is and you answer 4, that is a perfect answer 100% – you cannot get a higher standard of answer. However, something like keeping a garden weed-free is almost 100% impossible, so if you were to aim for a 100% weed-free garden that would be ridiculous.

Firstly, labelling yourself or others as a perfectionist is unhelpful. Every human has areas which they consider more important than others.

Susie is an English teacher and she is picky about grammar and spelling mistakes. However, when baking a cake she isn't that picky. For example, if the sugar or other ingredients are weighed slightly inaccurately, it doesn't bother her. Her friend Carol has accused Susie of being a perfectionist. Carol is a professional cook and measures all her ingredients to the nearest gram – if it is 1 gram over she will adjust the ingredients to be just right. And yet her use of English is much more flexible.

I have been called a perfectionist before, but I wouldn't spend ages writing out a shopping list on the computer, formatting it into a nice list, and spend ages choosing the correct font – it is not important to me, in fact I never write a shopping list. However, if I had to write a menu out for a wedding I might spend much more time and attention writing the menu and choosing a nice font.

Perfectionism is about how important something is to a person. We all have degrees of priority. What we need to do is access whether we have correctly prioritised aspects of our lives, and place them in order of importance.

We all are perfectionists just in different areas of our lives.

Because we all have different opinions about the levels of priority and importance it can be easy for there to be disagreements or discrepancies in opinion. We may sometimes end up being fearful of others and, as a result, let their priorities and levels of importance be dictated to us. It can then become a seeking approval game. *The Perfectionism Book* suggests that perfectionism is driven by the desire to be recognised and accepted. Whilst this is partly true, it is not necessarily always the case. For example, when cooking a meal for others I may spend more time and effort cooking for them than if I was cooking for myself – does that mean I am seeking approval? - not necessarily.

Beethoven used to meticulously count out sixty coffee beans every time he had a cup of coffee. Do you think that was seeking approval? No, probably he had an acute sense of taste and coffee was important to him. Not all perfectionism is driven by a desire to be recognised and accepted.

Perfectionism is not necessarily seeking approval

Perfectionism is not necessarily setting high goals

The Perfectionism Book suggests that perfectionism has three main traits:

1. Setting impossibly tough goals or high standards that can never be practically achieved.
2. Continuing to pursue these goals despite evidence of harm, usually to our own emotional health.
3. Basing our self-esteem partly or completely on whether we have met these goals.

Let's review point one in the list above: "Setting seemingly impossible goals". I have slight problems with this. My response is: have more faith. Have more faith in your idea and ability. Firstly, who is to judge what an impossibly tough goal is? According to this first point Edison's attempt at making the light bulb would be considered perfectionism. Other's might have thought he set himself a seemingly impossible tough goal. Where would we be in this world if pioneers and inventors had not stepped out and tried to achieve the so-called impossible?

Reviewing point two: "Pursue despite harm". Did those pioneers continue to pursue their goals? Of course they did. Did they face uncertainty, and difficulty? Yes of course. Did they have moments of worry, disappointment, or doubt if they couldn't achieve them? Most likely! Did they miss out on parties and other things in life? Yes, this is called sacrifice. If you never set any goals, you could completely avoid those kinds of emotional setbacks.

221

You haven't missed out, you've sacrificed.

The answer to point two is to persevere, try a new way of achieving your goal, and realise that sacrifices sometimes need to be made in order to achieve your goals, even emotional ones.

As an inventor, Edison made 1,000 unsuccessful attempts at inventing the light bulb. When a reporter asked, "How did it feel to fail 1,000 times?" Edison replied, "I didn't fail 1,000 times. The light bulb was an invention with 1,000 steps."

Don't try harder, try different.

A lot of people would probably have told Edison he was a perfectionist or he was attempting something that was impossible, but that was simply their lack of vision. I imagine after 600 attempts Edison may have doubted, worried or spent a few sleepless nights wondering whether he was wasting his time, but he continued despite the evidence of worry and potential harm to his health. He was willing to pay emotionally if he could eventually invent the light bulb. It's called sacrifice.

**People who call you a perfectionist
may just fail to understand your vision**

Finally, let's review point 3 in the list above "Basing your self-esteem on impossible goals". I am not sure what Edison's motives were. But I am certainly glad we have the light bulb. Yes, I agree with Dr Steel that our self-esteem shouldn't be rooted in our achievements – our self-esteem should be rooted in identity.

Famous Perfectionists

You can see this in the creative world. Directors such as Stanley Kubrick and Terrence Mallick might be described as perfectionists. What if we removed all the perfectionists from the world and world history? If you removed the perfectionists, you would take away 90% of the most notable people and all they have achieved; it would consequently be a very boring world to live in. Most classical musicians, most artists, top scientists, famous pioneers and inventors would cease to exist, Abraham Lincoln would meticulously rehearse and ruminate over his speeches, so we'd have to get rid of him too. It is thanks to the perfectionists that we have such things as technology. To a certain extent everyone is a perfectionist in their own little way – it's just a question of people's priorities and various areas of life. What is important to you? Look beyond the criticism, realise it is simply a difference in opinion. You can't control other people's opinions.

Perfectionist or Meticulous

In an earlier chapter we discussed how important language is. In some circumstances being "Perfectionist" is similar to "Meticulous", or "Conscientious". Perfectionism is also about how observant you are. You may have noticed a mistake in a painting that your friend hasn't seen; he may then call you a perfectionist but it is simply that you are being more observant.

So what exactly is perfectionism and when does it become bad for us?

**Perfectionism is imbalanced priorities.
Perfectionism is poor time management.**

Perfectionism simply is failing to have your priorities in the correct order. We have a variety of priorities in life that we can consider:

- The emotional cost to myself and others
- The financial cost to myself and others
- The cost to my relationships
- The cost to relationships between other people
- The cost in time of achieving the goal to myself and others
- The cost of procrastination
- The cost to my health
- The cost to my levels of tiredness
- The quality of what you are trying to achieve
- The quantity of what you are trying to achieve
- The permanency of the result - best is not a permanent state
- Physical energy
- Mental energy
- Safety
- Performance
- Features
- Reliability
- Conformance
- Durability
- Serviceability
- Aesthetics
- Understandability
- Recognition

Now if you are designing a nuclear power plant, "safety" might be the biggest priority, if you spend hours and hours trying to choose the colour of door paint and, as a result, you have less time to spend on designing the safety plans, then that is perfectionism because your priorities are incorrect.

I've spent quite a lot of time making a film, mainly because it is such a difficult task. Firstly, some people don't understand the enormity of the task so think I am a perfectionist. That is simply a misunderstanding. Secondly, I am interested in quality more than quantity; other film-makers may have different goals such as financial reward etc.

It is also worth bearing in mind that something might cost you a lot but be of huge benefit to others.

Janet is an entrepreneur, she's invented a new way to create safer and cleaner water. She travels with her team to countries all over the world and instils new water systems and educates the locals. She, however, is terrified of flying. According to *The Perfectionism Book* the following phrase would imply she needs to change her goals:

> "Continuing to pursue these goals despite evidence of harm, usually to our own emotional health."

Janet may put herself through a lot of worry and fear by flying on planes. However, she has two ways to view this:

1. This fear of flying is emotionally costly – I shouldn't do this.
2. This fear of flying is a sacrifice to achieve helping poor people in Africa. It's worth paying the emotional cost of flying to help these people.

When we step out and try new things we may face criticism. Thomas Edison faced a lot of criticism when inventing the light bulb. However, he kept going. The emotional cost he considered a sacrifice in comparison to the great reward.

Often we can become a perfectionist when making a decision. We can do this because we fear the consequences of making a wrong choice. But have you considered that the tension of perfectionism might be worse than making a wrong decision?

Perfectionist Pete spends two weeks researching where to go for a weekend trip. He is anxious about finding a good hotel, fearful that he will make a mistake. He finds a good hotel at £160 for the weekend. His wife is pleased.

Calm Christopher only spends a couple of hours researching where to go. He doesn't get anxious or stressed over finding a hotel. It's a pretty good hotel and cost £200 for the weekend. His wife is pleased.

It's a weekend trip. Yes Perfectionist Pete saves £40 compared to Christopher, but Calm Christopher saves two weeks of anxiety and stress. Was that extra time and tension (emotional cost) worth saving £40? For some maybe. Personally, I would rather have peace and more time than save £40.

Have you considered that the emotional cost caused by the:
- fear of rejection
- fear of criticism
- fear of making a bad decision

may actually be worse than the cost of:
- being rejected
- being criticised
- making a wrong decision

The stress I have in not making a decision may be greater than the criticism I might receive for making the wrong decision.

We have to weigh up the costs when making decisions. Often we forget to factor in emotional costs and the costs in time.

Also, note that the cost to relationships is on the list of priorities to consider. You may find that perfectionists can end up alienating their friends. Gerald constantly complains at school for not getting an "A" grade, "I'm such a failure" he keeps saying. His friend who really struggles to get a grade "C" now thinks "Well, if Gerald thinks he's a failure for not getting an A, what does he think of me?" Gerald ends up alienating his friends due to perfectionism. Of course, this can swing the other way where you never criticise or aim to improve anything in the fear that you'll put your friends down. Why are your grades such a high priority? What is most important to you?

When we are overly perfectionist in a particular area, we can struggle with depression because we have a tendency to blame ourselves for everything. We become so driven to achieve self-made goals that we become super sensitive to any failure or crisis. This is often simply because we have not sat down and thought about our priorities and their importance.

Sometimes being criticised as a perfectionist can result from differing patience levels. Bruckner and Brahms were criticised for being slow at finishing off their symphonies and yet they are now regarded highly in the music world. Their friends might have criticised them for taking time to write their music. Does that reflect more about their friends' lack of patience and short term vision, or does that reflect more about the perfectionism of Brahms and Bruckner? What is more important - quality or quantity? To the geniuses out there: you need to recognise that not everyone has been blessed with the same mental capacity, you may have to show some compassion to those who you consider less able.

Quality or Quantity

Remember that not everyone is blessed with a brain of a genius. Mozart may think that Beethoven was a perfectionist, procrastinator and slow at writing music, but that reflects more on Mozart's genius ability and incredible gift of writing quickly. Most of us are not Mozarts or geniuses in our fields, so we need to practise a little more patience. Priorities are really important, otherwise we can face burnout and depression. Consider the following?

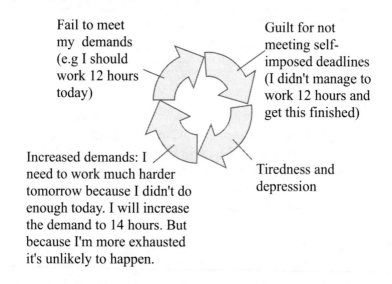

Fail to meet my demands (e.g I should work 12 hours today)

Guilt for not meeting self-imposed deadlines (I didn't manage to work 12 hours and get this finished)

Increased demands: I need to work much harder tomorrow because I didn't do enough today. I will increase the demand to 14 hours. But because I'm more exhausted it's unlikely to happen.

Tiredness and depression

What is the problem in the above scenario? Is it the standard of wanting to work 12 hours a day? Perhaps it is simply that work has become a higher priority than sleep.

A few questions to consider with perfectionism:
- If I put 200% more effort into something and only notice 10% distinguishable difference – is it worth it? If yes, why?

- How important is it? Why?

- Is quantity or quality more important here?

- What other things are more important? For example, if I have a deadline, is it more important to hit the deadline or more important to get the quality right?

- What do you want to prioritise here?

- What is the best use of your time?

- What are you willing to sacrifice?

- Are you a perfectionist because you are fearful of other people's response or seeking approval from others?

- Are your standards excessive, accurate, helpful and flexible?

- Are you using your time wisely?

- If you are trying to find out all the potential risks and problems before you start, will you ever start?

- And finally, if you wait until you're ready, will you ever start?

Perfectionism is a difficult topic to understand and write about. I hope what I have written was good enough!!

Control seeking

Control seeking can be a big issue for those who suffer with depression. Control seeking can lead to frustration and anger. To understand this subject we must first consider *why* we try to control other people, things and circumstances.

Firstly, trying to control someone is not a bad thing per se. During a fire, police may tape off an area in order to stop the public getting close to the fire. They are controlling people's movement, preventing them from getting near to danger. A fence near a cliff may control people from walking too near the edge. It's not that control seeking is particularly wrong, the issue is more about *what* you are trying to control, and the degree to which you try to control it.

Control and Responsibility

In order to understand control seeking we have to look at the topic of responsibility. Depression sufferers and perfectionists can often be criticised as being "Control Freaks." However, nobody ever gets called a "Responsibility Freak". That is because the word responsibility has a positive connotation but the word control can be a negative word.

> Controlling Claire is holding a charity concert and has hired a 100 seat hall. She wants to sell all the tickets and raise as much money as she can. She contacts as many of her friends as possible and asks them to buy tickets; she designs flyers and posters to a high quality. On the day of the concert only 90 tickets have been sold and only 80 people turn up. Naturally, we must praise her for hard work and her passion to raise money for the charity. However, she gets disappointed with the result because she has not sold all the 100 tickets. It is not that Claire is seeking control; it is _what_ she is seeking control of that is the problem. She has the control to contact her friends, and of how good the flyers and posters are, because she is designing them herself. However, she ultimately has no control over whether people will turn up to the concert having bought a ticket. She cannot force people to sit on the seat.

> Lazy Lucy tells her friends that Controlling Claire is a "Control Freak". However, when it is her turn to raise money at a charity event she fails to contact her friends and does a shoddy job at designing the poster. Only 30 tickets are sold and 20 people turn up. This does indeed show that Claire and Lucy must have had some control or responsibility in affecting the outcome but they don't have ultimate control.

Understanding control is about understanding your responsibilities. If you have some responsibility over the outcome, then clearly you must have some control.

The danger of calling someone a control freak is that you end up criticising their desires which can be very painful for the person. It is like telling them that they shouldn't have those desires or hopes.

Lucy called Claire a "control freak", but this doesn't encourage Claire; it actually instils despair, as it is a criticism of her hopes and desires. It is not that Claire's desires are necessarily wrong; her desire to raise lots of money should be highly regarded. Nonetheless, her sense of responsibility and control is not healthy.

Control is about understanding your level of responsibility

If our hope only lies in favourable circumstances, or trying to alter something that we have no right or ability to change or control, then we are going to suffer a lot of disappointment. What exactly do you want to achieve? Have you considered the costs?

Control and Delegation

Control can of course be delegated to others. If you are an orchestra conductor you simply can't play all the instruments at once and control the outcome of the performance. The individual expressions, note tunings and phrasing are carried out by the musicians. Control is also about working out what you wish to delegate and the amount of trust you have in other people to do a good job.

Can you imagine a world where you had zero control, or you relinquished all your control to others – delegating all your tasks? Imagine being a film director and relinquishing 100% control, giving every single decision to someone else, and ending up sitting on a beach in the Caribbean not doing anything at all. How much hope would you have in the final film? Probably none. How rewarding would your project be? Probably not very rewarding. Giving too much delegation to others could steal hope. Some degree of control or responsibility is required in order to have hope.

In contrast, never delegating tasks to others could equally lead to burn-out and steal hope. If you've been repeatedly been let down by others, there may be a tendency to want to control the outcome by doing everything yourself. This is not healthy. Control is a good thing as long as it is manageable and balanced.

You may want to consider the following questions:

- How can you delegate tasks?
- Am I delegating too much or too little?
- What things in life are you struggling with that you could delegate?
- Who can you delegate tasks to?
- If you delegate a task and it is not completed to a satisfactory level, how will you respond?
- What are the benefits of delegation?

Control and Threat

"Threat" normally determines the degrees to which we try to control. This is particularly evident in situations where we try to control people's opinions.

If someone said that I would never get a job because I had a green face, I would not feel a need to control their opinion.

232

Firstly, I know that it isn't true, and secondly, if that person tells someone else this statement, I am not convinced others would believe it. As a result, their opinion poses no threat to me.

I believe I am an honest person. If, however, a person said to me that I would never get a job because I'm a liar, I would be bothered by their opinion. This is because if they relayed their opinion to others, it would pose a threat to my reputation and relationships. So the level of threat determines our desire to control.

Note here that truth doesn't always affect the level of control we want to exercise. My friend is going to tell a girl I want to date that I have six points on my driving licence. If it is true, I feel threatened because I think the girl might hold that information against me. If it is false, I still feel threatened because I think the girl may listen, believe the information, and still hold it against me.

If "threat" determines the level of control, then how do we reach a place where we don't feel threatened by others opinions?

The fact is we cannot control other people's opinions of us. We could put a gun to someone else's head and make them say the opposite, but nobody's opinion can ultimately be controlled. We can only influence opinion.

We cannot control other people's opinions.
Any attempt to do so will leave us frustrated.

Knowing your vision, likes, dislikes, opinions, and how your emotions work are all part of building self-esteem and identity. As we build those we will find that we become less bothered by other's opinions.

233

**"Live in such a way that if someone spoke badly
of you, no one would believe it."**[33]

Control and Justice

Besides our understanding of responsibility and threat, control
is also related to our sense of justice. If someone is put in
prison for telling a joke, and a murderer gets away with his
crime, we will want to control those situations because we are
annoyed at a lack of justice.

What is justice? The Oxford dictionary defines "Justice" as
"The quality of being fair and reasonable.".[34] The opposite of
justice in a negative sense is "Getting away with it"; in a
positive sense it could be "Mercy". The issue of justice is a
controversial one. Who or what determines what is just? How
can we measure justice?

Firstly, none of us will see justice in the same way. Our
perception of justice will be filtered by our own experiences.
Consider the following:

1. Lily always behaved well at school but her classmates
   framed her. Lily's teacher was always telling her off for
   things she hadn't done.
2. Sophia always misbehaved at school. But she framed
   other students. She got away with all of her bad
   behaviour.
3. Aria sometimes misbehaved at school. Her teacher was
   always being merciful and letting her off the hook.

These girls' concept of justice and mercy will be filtered by
their experiences. We all have filters. Our perception of justice
will impact _what_ or _who_ it is we want to control, and _why_ we
want to control that thing or person.

If I don't believe I've been given justice in life, I may attempt to bring justice by controlling others.

We all want justice. However, a lot of us want mercy too. How can we live in a world full of justice and mercy? <u>Can we have both</u>?

If you want to live in a world where everyone faces "justice with no mercy", then that would mean you'd never be shown mercy. If you want to live in a world where you are shown mercy and little justice, then that would mean there would be a lot of mercy for others too. You cannot expect to live in a world where everyone else receives "justice with no mercy" and you receive "mercy with no justice". We all live in the same world.

If you focus on the lack of justice, it will lead to depression and despair. Instead, focus on the times when you've been shown mercy.

Where in life have you been shown mercy?

Control and Retaliation

Another issue that can result in unhealthy levels of control is when we ourselves feel that we have been controlled. If we have been controlled, we may react positively by standing up for ourselves. However, being controlled can sometimes lead to unhealthy reactions: rebellion, retaliation or trying to exert power over someone. For example, if a boss at work is very controlling, someone may feel inferior and not in control of their life. As a result, they may try to regain ground, to reassert their power by trying to control something else. They may, for example, then try to control their wife with nasty threats.

Control and Suffering

We will often try to control because we fear suffering. Control is often based on the following lies:

> "I can't control and determine what will happen
> in my life, therefore I am going to suffer."

> "If I can control my life, I will not suffer"

We think that if we can control our lives we are less likely to suffer. But ironically, we may suffer more from the tension of trying to control. Besides, why would a little control make you happier? You didn't control where you were born, you didn't control how this planet formed, you can't control the weather, you can't control the traffic? 99.9999% of the world you cannot control – and that is an underestimation. Why would having an extra 0.0001% of control make you happier?

**If you focus on what you can't
control, it will lead to anger.**

Instead focus on what you can control.

Control and Goals

A blocked goal can lead to anger and depression because we feel out of control. In our earlier example, Claire's goal was as follows:

> "I have to sell 100 tickets and must have everyone
> sitting on those 100 seats."

Even if they have bought a ticket, Claire cannot force people to come to the concert, and therefore she cannot ultimately control whether her goal is met or not. If she realigned her goal to something that is more dependent on her ability, and less on others, she will most likely prevent herself from disappointment. For example, she could set a much more feasible goal as follows:

> "I would like to sell 100 tickets, but there is no guarantee I will. Therefore, my goal will be to design a poster and flyers to the best of my ability, contact as many friends and people as possible, and try to relax and enjoy preparing for this concert".

In redefining a goal, a goal needs to be a "SMART" goal; "Specific, Measurable, Attainable, Relevant and Timely". Claire's initial goal was unhealthy because it was unlikely to be attainable. The opposite of a SMART goal is a "VAGUE" goal; "Vague, Absurd Goal with Unreasonable, Expectations".

If a goal is vague, it is very difficult to complete and we have no sense of closure. Can you imagine playing a game of football with ten different goals rather than two specific goals for each team? That would be very frustrating. Can you imagine if you had to play blindfolded and when you scored a goal the referee wouldn't tell the team? That would mean you would have no sense of measuring the score. The blindfolds would make it difficult to attain the goal. What if you asked the referee how long the match was and he told you "I'm not sure"? That would be a recipe for depression; you would have very little sense of control.

Turn goals from VAGUE goals into SMART goals.

Some further examples of redefining goals are as follows:

Initial goal: I want people to like my film.

Problem: I cannot control whether people like my film. There are so many people and different opinions. Certain films seem to only appeal to women, and others, like war films, seem to

237

appeal more to the male psyche. There are people who hate the films I love. This goal is wrong on so many levels:

1. *The goal is not specific:* What does it mean for "people to like my film"?
2. *The goal is not easily measurable:* How do you measure whether a film is likeable? If everyone gives it a rating of more than 6 out of 10, or if 100 people give it a 10 out of 10 rating – which of these is the goal?
3. *The goal is not attainable:* This goal is too reliant on other people. It would better to have a goal that is more personally focused.
4. *The goal is not relevant:* How and to what is this goal relevant?
5. *The goal is not timely:* How long will it take for people to like my film? If I haven't had 100 people ask for an autograph after the first week of box office openings, does that mean that the goal has failed?

Redefined goal: I would like people who are depressed (specific) to learn that they are not alone in this problem (measurable and attainable). I would like them to respond after they have watched the film by seeking further advice e.g. taking a business card, purchasing a book etc., or visiting a website (timely).

A further example:

Initial goal: I am going on holiday to Wales next week. I want to go to the beach and sunbathe.

Problem: It's Wales! Guaranteeing sun is something that is not controllable.

Redefined goal: I am going on holiday to Wales next week. I am going to make my best effort to enjoy the weather. If it is sunny, I will sunbathe. If it rains, I can take a book to read.

Owning Control

When we talk about control we often use the verb "to have". For example, "I have control of my finances". The word "have" implies ownership. In that way do we believe we own control? Do we "own" control? If we see control as something to own, does that change our perspective on how we treat control? Perhaps there is a tendency to think that the more we can control, the more secure we feel.

Control and Priorities

When we gain control in one area we will often lose control in another. Our sense of control is not necessarily about *how* much we have, but *what* we deem to be important. Consider the following:

> If I could control the weather, and that took 24 hours of my time, and if I could control the traffic on the road, which also took 24 hours of my time, then if I subsequently try to control the weather 100 percent, I would be relinquishing control over the traffic. If I tried to control the traffic 50 percent, then I would be giving up 50 percent control over the weather.

In real life this may be less obvious. It could be that a student is living with parents. He feels he has little control over what he can do. He can seldom invite friends home for parties, because his parents need to go to bed earlier. In doing so, he may feel he is controlled by his parents. He could move to his own flat and gain control over his social life. However, in doing so, he may give up some sense of control over his finances; he may have a more expensive rent to pay and hence have less control over how he spends his money. In this way, control is about priorities.

**In order to gain control in one area
you will often have to give up
control in another area.**

When it is beyond control

Sometimes we want to control things that are seemingly beyond our control. What if you genuinely need someone's help and they fail to help you? For example, what if you knew someone had the answer to your problem but they refused to help you? Or what if you were short of a penny and you knew the person next to you had a penny, but they failed to give it to you when you asked for it? Situations like this can be very frustrating and you may want to take control – to somehow force these people to help you. How can we respond in such situations?

Firstly, assess your responsibility: you may have more control over the outcome than you realise. It may be there is some other approach you could take which you haven't tried. Failing that you have to let go, realise you've done your best, and trust that there is someone looking out for you.

**"We can't control the world; but we
can control our reactions to it."**[35]

Preparation

A lack of preparation can contribute to depression. If you're trying to write a piece of music in the style of Mozart but haven't studied Mozart in detail you may find you get extremely frustrated and depressed that your music doesn't sound like Mozart. If you start to paint but you haven't cleaned your brushes, mixed the colours, worked out which brushes you need to use etc. you may find that this leads to frustration and anger. Writers will often spend hours brainstorming ideas before even starting to pen the first page. Preparation is key to lowering your levels of stress and disappointment.

Lack of understanding learning curves

One thing that a lot of people fail to realise is that there is a learning curve in all aspects of life. David Dunning and Justin Kruger have performed studies into how people perceive the difficulty of various tasks. The Dunning-Kruger[36] effect explains some interesting concepts to the learning curve – namely that we often incorrectly perceive the difficulty of tasks. One thing I truly believed when making my film was that the more I learnt the quicker I would get at making the film. This was a failure to understand the learning curve. In fact, as you learn more there is a tendency to slow down, not speed up. Failure to understand this can actually lead you to beat yourself up, thinking, "I should be getting faster".

When a child is given a single shade of blue paint and a single paintbrush and asked to paint a sky they will do it fairly quickly. Let's say five minutes. They have a fairly high level of confidence. As they start to learn more about painting they will increase their knowledge and also their tools. Now they have "Cobalt blue, Ultramarine, and Cerulean blue." and three types of brush. They now have more choice. The child never questioned "What blue shall I use for the sky?" or "which brush shall I use?" because they didn't have that choice. As they mature they now need to figure out which blue they like to use best. As an adult they may study well-known painters such as Turner and Constable, work out what brushes and colours they used, and experiment with different techniques. This means that as the adults' knowledge increases, their tools and choices also increase, and their time for studying also increases. They are faced with more decisions and choices and consequently will take longer to paint. Eventually, when painters become extremely proficient at what they do, and have developed their style, they will stop learning, stop acquiring new tools, and have fewer decisions to make. Their decisions are made quickly by their developed style. Therefore, the proficient painter starts speeding up again.

If you fail to understand the learning curve, then you are more likely to beat yourself up, give up or feel low about your ability.

> "When we start to learn any new thing, like French, or golf, or public speaking, we never advance steadily. We do not improve gradually. We do it by sudden jerks, by abrupt starts. Then we remain stationary a time, or we may even slip back and lose some of the ground we have previously gained. These periods of stagnation, or retrogression, are well known by all psychologists; and they have been named 'plateaux in the curve of learning'. Students of public speaking will sometimes be stalled for weeks on one of these plateaux. Work as hard as they may, they cannot get off it. The weak ones give up in despair."[37]

**"Every activity worth doing
has a learning curve."**
Seth Godin

Work Life Balance

Being too busy can lead to depression because you end up exhausted. We are more prone to negative thoughts when tired. In this book we have described memory working similar to muscle reflexes. When you get physically tired your body reflexes slow down; it is the same with our mental reflexes. Our memory recall is slower and less effective.

Rest is important to allow our memory reflexes to work effectively. We need to make sure we allow time for our brains to re-energise. An hour's lunch is ideal because it takes 30 minutes for us to properly wind down and another 30 minutes to re-energise.

Remember, when we rest, we need to rest properly. That might sound like a strange statement. However, when we do our hobbies we can often let perfectionism creep in and this may affect our ability to relax and enjoy the situation. As mentioned previously, I sometimes play snooker to relax. I'm not particularly good. If I have a mindset that I need to get a bigger score than last time, that can encroach on my ability to relax.

Many people find it hard to relax and enjoy themselves. Surprisingly a lot of people don't have hobbies. In addition, it is possible that hobbies can lose their vibrancy – becoming stale and meaningless. Sometimes we can find ourselves being over-competitive, following hobbies just because our friends pursue them, or continue hobbies through habit; doing so will only corrode our levels of enjoyment. Therefore, it is important to consider how, when, where, why, and with whom you relax most. Rejuvenate your hobbies.

Busyness has in recent years been given a bad name. A few of my friends almost boast about the number of hours they work – giving the impression that if you are working you are successful and not lazy. On the contrary, if you are a workaholic and constantly busy it probably means the following:

- You find it hard to say no to things.
- You have poor time management.
- You haven't sorted out your priorities in life.
- You find silence or relaxation difficult.
- You haven't learnt to listen to yourself.
- You haven't considered the importance of relationships, family and friends.

Some people are scared of silence. When they are not busy

they don't know how to relax. Busyness can be a mask for not wanting to stop and consider life. Some people are too scared of self-examination and considering questions like "why am I here?" so simply keep working. Why do some people boast about being busy? Here are some possible reasons:

1. **Pride.**
   Hey look at me, I have so many contracts and so many people want to employ me, therefore I must be someone significant, I must be someone special.

2. **Fear**
   If I stop working so hard, someone might steal all my contracts. I must say yes to everything otherwise my competition will get ahead of me.

3. **Greed**
   I simply keep working because I want more money. I want a bigger house and I don't want the competition to succeed.

Being too busy can be corrosive. However, we are not meant to be lazy. If we spend huge amounts of time on our own and not working, it can leave a lot of time and space for negative thoughts to ruminate and fester. Not only does work give you a sense of purpose, but it also helps build relationships and focus your mind away from yourself. Striking a work life balance is key.

> **"Never get so busy making a living**
> **that you forget to make a life."**
> *Dolly Parton*

> **"We make a living by what we get.**
> **We make a life by what we give."**
> *Winston Churchill*

Self-Esteem, Self-Awareness & Identity

Self-esteem and self-awareness are very important factors in building hope. Who are you? What is your identity? Why do you do what you do? Why do you believe what you believe? What are the reasons and motivations for what you do? It is impossible to know everything about yourself, but we can strive to learn more.

Self-esteem and our sense of identity are based on three core needs: Significance, Acceptance and Security. Often we make false conclusions about how to achieve these:

Significance = Performance + Accomplishments
Acceptance = Appearance + Admiration + Value
Security = Health + Material Wealth + Status

Ideally, our three core needs should be rooted in relationship:

Significance = Relationship
Acceptance = Relationship
Security = Relationship

Significance

Let's look at significance. Every human is significant. Out of the millions of sperm that swam to the egg you were the first. You are significant because you exist. How significant is a one month year old baby? It won't have achieved much yet, but it is extremely significant to the parents. Just as no two snowflakes are identical, every human is unique and individual.

You are significant simply because you are you

**It's not <u>what</u> we do that determines <u>who</u> we are,
it's <u>who</u> we are that determines <u>what</u> we do.**

245

When we think of being significant we tend to think of great accomplishments and high levels of performance. Not everyone can be a world-renowned scientist, musician or medical surgeon. We often overlook the small things where results aren't obvious.

I remember a friend Russell walking past a bicycle left outside a restaurant. The owner had left his lights on. Russell made the effort to switch them off. It was only a small thing, but it could have saved the cyclist's life. If the cyclist had come out of the restaurant several hours later and cycled home with the batteries drained, he could have been knocked off and killed. Each little action and choice can set off a chain reaction. The film "Pay it forward" greatly shows that it is not always the big cheese who is the most significant. How often do we talk about Einstein's mother? Beethoven's father? Steven's Spielberg's school teachers? They were significant in their own way.

**Don't underestimate the
significance of the small things.**

**Few people thank Einstein's mother and
father for doing something significant.**

**A penny may seem insignificant when
it's on its own but when you are a
penny short, it means everything.**

Acceptance
Our understanding and sense of acceptance is vital to mental health. *Experiencing* rejection, *fearing* rejection, or *feeling* that you are not accepted, are major causes of depression. Remember, feelings may not <u>always</u> reflect the truth.

We all want to be accepted, but how do we define acceptance?

Also, how do we define rejection? Without having some clear definitions we may, at times, feel the following:

> "I'm looking for acceptance but I don't know what acceptance is."

If you feel unaccepted and believe the above, it will be like chasing your tail in circles. Considering this, it is really important to define "acceptance".

When measure acceptance we need to make sure we don't have double standards. Our definition of acceptance should apply to others as well as ourselves. Do you have any friends who are ugly, fat or who don't have a great appearance by your standards? Do you accept them? And yet you might feel that others won't accept you unless you live up to those same standards. Often we can have a double standard when it comes to appearance. For example:

- I can accept overweight people.
- People won't accept me because I'm overweight.

The above is damaging. Firstly, it is a double standard. And secondly, it is basing acceptance on appearance. Should we be measuring acceptance by appearance? I don't believe so.

Sadly we can often come to the wrong conclusions of what acceptance is and how we measure it. Let's look at some ways people falsely try to gain acceptance.

Appearance
We often falsely base acceptance on appearance. However, consider the following:

A geode is a rock that looks fairly normal on the outside but when you crack it open there are often amethyst crystals inside. Just like a geode we can tend to value our self-worth on external appearances. As we start to recognise that we are beautiful inside, it can help alleviate depression and give us hope for the future.

There are many famous people who are overweight or not particularly good looking that are accepted; so our value should not be intrinsically linked to appearance.

<u>Circumstances</u>
Sometimes we can think that our circumstances can define our value and acceptance. This is shallow.

Take a five million pound diamond and put it in a shop window. How much is it worth? Five million pounds. Now take that diamond and throw it against a wall. How much is it worth? Five million pounds. Hit the diamond. Kick it across the floor. Shout abuse at it. How much is it worth? Five million pounds. Would I accept that diamond as a present – yes of course. No matter what you go through in life you are still of great value. No matter what your circumstances you will always be worthy of acceptance.

**A diamond retains its value no matter
what it goes through, and yet you
are much more valuable than diamonds.**

Finances

Ideally, we don't want people to accept us just for our money. Rich people may think they are accepted, but may find their friends walk away if they suddenly lose all their money.

Approval Seeking

Constantly looking for approval and judging yourself by others opinions is going to steal your hope. Because there are so many opinions, we can end up going up and down like a yo-yo. What if one of your friends thinks that blue clothes suit you and dislikes red clothes, what if another friend loves red clothes, but hates blue. You simply can't please everyone.

**Those who try to please everyone
end up going round in circles.**

When we try to actively look for acceptance it often becomes approval seeking. By doing so we are put our fate in the hands of others. Do you want other's opinions to control your life?

So if the above are false ways of trying to find acceptance, how do we genuinely find and experience acceptance?

Finding Acceptance

Firstly, I believe a lot of feelings of not being accepted stem from having a lack of vision. Do you think a fireman worries about what people will think of his shoes when he's running into a building to rescue someone? No. If you have a strong focus, you probably won't give two hoots what others think of you. If you want to overcome approval seeking and rejection, focus on your vision.

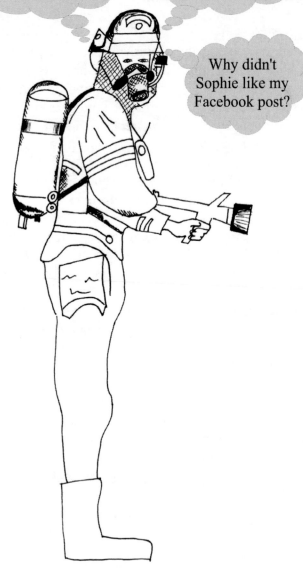

When we have vision our worries subside.
Get vision.

Secondly, we need to alter our understanding of acceptance. There are two ways to view it.

1. Acceptance is something distant that we have to find.
   Imagine that there is a lot of water on the planet Saturn. You see the water as distant and something you have to find or bring to yourself. This is often how we see acceptance – we see it as something distant that we have to find.

2. Acceptance is close
   Imagine you are sitting next to a tap full of fresh cold water. In order to feel the water, you need to realise you have already got it, and then switch on the tap. Acceptance is similar. You already have acceptance in some shape or form – you just need to realise it and act accordingly. Note here that even if you recognise you are accepted, you still need to act on it; this is the equivalent of switching on the tap.

I believe we need to alter our understanding of acceptance so that we adopt the second viewpoint.

**You are already accepted in
some shape or form.**

Let's look at an example of this:

A party is held in a house. The guests are all very accepting and know each other. A stranger, George, arrives at the party. He views acceptance in the first way. He feels he has to find acceptance from the other people there. George spends ages trying to crack jokes to win people's approval. He is like the person trying to find water on Saturn.

251

Later on another stranger, Liam, arrives at the party. He holds the second viewpoint. Liam believes everyone already accepts him, but waits for people to talk to him. He is like the person who has realised that the water is next to him, but has failed to act on that belief and turn the tap. Liam, therefore, doesn't experience acceptance.

Later still, our third character, Peter, arrives at the party. He also holds the second viewpoint. He believes that everyone accepts him so makes an effort to talk to others. He not only believes people accept him, but he actually acts on it. Peter is like the person who realises the tap is next to him and switches it on to experience it.

**Assume everyone accepts you
until proven otherwise.**

Act upon your beliefs

With depression we tend to see things as black and white. As a result, there can be a tendency to see "acceptance" in this way. For example, we may say "Stacey" accepts me, but "Colin" doesn't. Firstly, we must acknowledge that acceptance grows as you get to know someone. Secondly, we must realise that acceptance is partially blind.

Acceptance is partially blind

When we accept someone we accept them on the basis of what we know about them. Consider the following:

I meet a man called John at a party. He seems nice. He talks about photography, something that I am passionate about. He seems polite, honest and kind. Our friendship blossoms over time. My acceptance of him is based on everything I know of him at the time. A few months later I find out he has been involved in a scam and he is selling fraudulent insurance. My initial acceptance of John was partially blind; I was accepting him on what I knew about him at the time. At this point I have a choice whether to continue accepting him, and on what terms. Perhaps I will distance myself for a period, or perhaps I will withdraw completely, or perhaps I will continue my relationship if I feel he is remorseful or I can be of some help in the situation. Let's say I continued to accept him, but not accept his actions. A year passes and I then find out his fraudulent ways have been funding a violent gang of criminals in London. Now I know more about him and have a choice whether I continue accepting him.

This is an extreme example, whereby John's character is slowly uncovered revealing his darker side. In other circumstances, as we get to know someone, they may reveal more and more beauty, and we may come to accept them even more. However, notice that acceptance is a choice. At each stage, when more information is revealed to us about the person's character and actions, we need to reassess the situation appropriately.

Acceptance is a choice

Did you stay in contact with everyone from school? Most likely not. Did you reject them because they were horrible, uninteresting, insignificant people? No. You simply had to move on with your life; you cannot maintain every relationship. On the flip side, this is why other people may seemingly reject you. It's not that you are insignificant or boring, it is simply that they cannot maintain being friends with everyone. When you experience feelings of rejection, don't leap to the conclusion that you must have some character flaw.

Can you imagine if you tried to stay in contact with every school-friend and work colleague? It would simply blow your mind. There is a difference between "a relationship naturally ending" and "rejecting someone".

<u>Rejection</u>
Remember that we often jump to conclusions about rejection. Openly talking about rejection can be difficult but if you are really struggling with a particular person have you considered talking to them about it? You may want to find a mediator or someone to discuss this with. For example, if you have issues of feeling rejected by your mother-in-law but you get along well with your father-in-law, sharing your feelings may be a way to move on with your life.

**It's okay to talk about your feelings
of rejection. It may help you to move on.**

<u>Self-acceptance</u>
When we reflect on the topic of acceptance there are two distinct categories:

1. Acceptance by others
2. Self-acceptance

So far we have generally been talking about "Acceptance by others". But we also need to consider "Self-Acceptance". It is important not to confuse the two. Sometimes the following can be a problem:

> In order to feel accepted by others, I need to accept myself first. But in order to accept myself, I need to be accepted by others.

A lot of the points raised about dealing with others can also be applied:

1. *Acceptance is partially blind:*
   Whilst we know a lot more about ourselves than others, we don't know everything about ourselves. We do not always know our hidden motives, why we like certain things, and what fears we have. We therefore accept ourselves on what we know.

2. *Acceptance is a choice:*
   We choose to accept ourselves knowing our good and bad traits. If we are waiting to be perfect before we accept ourselves, it will never happen.

Let's look at an example of this:

At school Jamie found writing difficult, and at university his lecturers criticised his essays; saying that they didn't flow. Because Jamie feels inferior in this area, he is fearful about writing a book; he feels that his writing style might be ridiculed.

Firstly, *acceptance is partially blind*. Jamie needs to accept that he will never fully know how people will respond to his book until he writes it.

Secondly, *acceptance is a choice*. Jamie has taken some lessons in writing and improved. He needs to accept that whilst his writing might not be perfect, it is much better. He needs to choose to write a book despite his insecurities. If Jamie waits for his skills to be perfect, he will never start.

In accepting yourself, it is important to realise that having difficulties can have benefits. Having flaws or difficulties means that we become more reliant on others. If Jamie's writing style was perfect, he would never have to ask others for feedback. By having flaws it means we build meaningful relationships. This is true in reverse. Your strengths complement other's weaknesses.

We complement each other

In addition, if Jamie had been able to write perfectly at the age of five, he would never have been able to celebrate progress. When he finishes his book, he can compare it to his shoddy university essays and enjoy the achievement.

Our weaknesses allow us to celebrate progress

In accepting oneself, it is much easier to be thankful for the positive aspects and events in life. It is much harder to accept the negative. Paul likes that he is tall, has blue eyes, and was born in England. It is much harder for him to accept that he doesn't like the shape of his chin and that he recently failed to start his own business.

There are two areas that are hard to accept:
1. Accepting permanent things
   Paul will always have the same chin.

   Mass produced items have less value. Ikea furniture might have perfectly laser cut corners, but a hand-carved table, without perfectly cut corners, has much more value. There are no two identical people on earth, and it is the differences that make you so valuable.

2. Accepting your temporary status
   Paul feels that life has dealt him a bad hand. He finds it hard that his own business has failed.

   If it is temporary, then it can change. Yes, life might have dealt you a bad hand, but complaining about the hand you have been given isn't going to allow you move forward.

> "God, grant me the serenity to
> accept the things I cannot change,
> Courage to change the things I can,
> And wisdom to know the difference."
> *Reinhold Niebuhr*

Security

A lot of people rely on money and health to feel secure. If their bank balance is dwindling or health is failing they may feel insecure. But being poor and coping is actually more secure than being rich. Let me explain:

Jill is on benefits and has to scrape a living on £50 a week. She works out a strategy on how she can live on soup and potatoes. She downgrades her phone tariff and cancels various luxuries. She finds hobbies that are free such as reading books in the library. And she manages to survive.

Ten years later Jill finds herself in a well paid career with a salary over £100k a year. After the company collapses her colleagues feel extremely insecure, they simply don't know how to cope and are fearful of the future. Jill is not that bothered, she has remembered the time when she survived on minimal amounts; if she's done it before she can do it again. Jill has plenty of hope for the future.

> **Security is about being able to
> survive with nothing, not about
> having a lot. The higher up you are,
> the further you have to fall.**

> **Security is not about having things;
> it's about handling things.**

Security also comes through relationships. If you have absolutely nothing but have strong relationships what is there to fear? If you want to be secure, it is better to focus your efforts on building relationships, then you will never have to fear not having a roof over your head, food to eat or water to drink.

It has been said that a man gets his identity from his work, and a women from bearing children. What if a man loses his job? What if a woman can't bear children? These things in themselves shouldn't define us. There is much more to life than these things. Don't get stuck at the roadblock, find a new route. You are ultimately much more Significant, Accepted and Secure than you realise.

Sources
People around us have a big influence on what we think and feel. Our thoughts and views of acceptance, significance and security can be adopted from them. Authority figures (teachers and religious leaders) and particularly your parents tend to have the biggest influence.

Remember, parents are not perfect and they will, to some degree, pass their unhealthy beliefs onto their children. In this way, some mental health issues are inherited by nurture. That may sound like I am blaming parents for mental health issues. Whilst there may be an element of truth that your mental health can derive from your parents, let us remember that blame is not useful. Remember, blame is a waste of energy that could be otherwise diverted into fixing a problem, learning how to cope with a situation, or starting afresh.

By and large, there are three main ways in which unhealthy beliefs can be transferred:

1. *Direct Transfer:*
   For example, a mother says to her child: "You can't go to the party in that outfit. It looks dreadful."

2. *Indirect Transfer via Self-Criticism:*
   For example, a mother says to herself whilst in front of her child: "I can't go to the party in this outfit. It looks dreadful. I won't fit in."

3. *Indirect Transfer via Criticising others:*
   For example, a mother says to her child: "No wonder uncle Andrew isn't married. Look at his outfit."

In each of the instances above a child may easily jump to the conclusion "If I don't wear appropriate outfits, I won't be accepted". Worse still they may believe there is some generic clothing standard to live up to. To spend a life chasing an undefined standard can end up causing a lot of grief and pain.

Take some time to write down your parents and your own beliefs and characteristics. A table has been provided on the following page. However, you may want to use a separate piece of paper.

If it is possible, talk about your mental health with your parents; compare your beliefs and complete the table. You may learn something valuable about your parents and yourself.

Our beliefs about Significance, Acceptance
and Security are often unknowingly
adopted from our parents.

My father's positive beliefs about Significance, Acceptance and Security	My mother's positive beliefs about Significance, Acceptance and Security	My own positive beliefs about Significance, Acceptance and Security

My father's negative beliefs about Significance, Acceptance and Security	My mother's negative beliefs about Significance, Acceptance and Security	My own negative beliefs about Significance, Acceptance and Security

Note here that there are potentially a lot of crossovers. You may have adopted these without taking time to consider them. This happens as children because we have a deep need to be accepted by parents. As a result, we can adopt unhealthy attitudes knowingly and unknowingly. Consider the following:

When Liam was ten years old his father told him to cheat during his maths test. His father wanted him to get a good result. Despite Liam knowing cheating was wrong, his deep need to feel accepted by his father overrode his beliefs and he went ahead and cheated. As a result, Liam may have learnt that "It is okay to cheat." Worse still he may have learnt "If I cheat, I will do better, and people will accept me". This is an example of knowingly adopting an unhealthy belief. However, the more dangerous beliefs are the subtle hidden ones.

When Emma was six years old she witnessed her mother getting paranoid whilst crossing roads. Because we are wired for empathy and connect by feeling the same emotion, Emma adopted a fear of crossing roads. She did this subconsciously to connect with her mother and feel more accepted. This is known as the "Offspring Stockholm Syndrome" effect.

One of the biggest effects our parents have on our psyche is that they shape our view of different genders. Our father will be our arch-stereotype of a man. Our mother will be our arch-stereotype of a mother. For example, if a mother is demanding and not accepting of men, and a father is busy and absent, we will tend to conclude beliefs similar to the following.

1. "My mother is demanding, therefore all women are demanding."
2. "My mother is not accepting of men, therefore all women are not accepting of men."
3. "My mother is not accepting of men, therefore all men

261

are useless and not good enough for women."

4. "My mother is not accepting of men. Men are fine, therefore women are weird."

5. "My father is busy and absent, therefore all men are busy and absent."

Take the first three beliefs. Ethan's mother is demanding of men, and therefore Ethan subconsciously believes that all women are demanding. This makes it very difficult for Ethan to go on dates. Every time he meets a girl he is thinking "I am not good enough – I can't meet her demands – she won't accept me". Sadly, these beliefs may get strengthened when Ethan faces unrequited love. He will look at the girl who has rejected him and conclude, "This proves that I am not good enough – that women are demanding and will never accept me".

Alternatively, if Ethan believes the fourth belief, his experiences may reinforce that belief and render him hopeless: "I'm fine; the rejection proves that women never accept men. I can't do anything about it – it's all their fault."

The important thing to ask is whether these traits are common to different genders or whether they are simply individual traits.

If Ethan is also demanding, or a male teacher at school is demanding, he could conclude the following:

My mother is demanding of herself and others. I am demanding of myself and others. And my male teacher is demanding of himself and others. This means that being "demanding" is not a male or female trait. My father is not demanding. Therefore, it is possible for people not to be demanding. My belief that "all women are demanding" is not true – it just happens to be the case with my own mother.

Let's look at an example for a daughter. Amelia is six years old. Her father is always busy working and he never gives her time and attention. He doesn't give her time with her homework or read stories to her. However, when Amelia digs into her box of fancy dress clothes and comes downstairs in a variety of outfits she gets attention from her father. As a result, Amelia believes "My father is busy and absent and only pays attention when I dress up for him, therefore all men are too busy and absent, and in order to get their attention I must dress up in a certain way." As Amelia grows up she is caught in a vicious cycle of trying to get men's attention through wearing clothes. When she doesn't get attention she concludes that her clothes are just not good enough. This sadly reinforces her belief. She thinks "if only I had such and such a dress, then...". However, she ends up in a cycle of debt. Amelia needs to consider whether her belief is typical of men, or whether it can be found in both women and men. Is this a trait of just her father and some others?

> My father is busy and only gives his attention to me when I dress for him. My boyfriend acts likewise. So this may seem like a male trait. However, my friend Chloe is always too busy for me and also only pays attention to me when I wear clothes to receive attention. Therefore, busyness and getting attention via dressing up is not a male or female trait. Furthermore, my friend James comments on how great I look when I am wearing the plainest clothes, and uncle Mike is never too busy. I do not have to dress up to get their attention. It's just my dad and boyfriend that seem that way, plus a few others.

263

Can you see something similar in your own life? What beliefs of male and female genders have you made assumptions about based on your parents?

Personality Type

A while ago I spoke to someone who had two children. He mentioned how the children were quite polarised in terms of their outlook on life. Owen was optimistic but Peter was pessimistic. He was convinced they had different personality types. "Why would they be so different if they have been raised by the same family?" he asked. I can see his predicament. However, there is an assumption here that "children in a family are equally raised and therefore should end up similar".

We know that despite children being raised by the same parents, children could drastically differ in their outlook on life because it is not the only factor involved. Here are some factors which may lead to differing personalities within a family.

Influence of others

Parents aren't the only people who raise children. Teachers in school, books and television can drastically change the outlook of a child's cognitive development. Children in a family may have different friendships and company. Do not be deceived – bad company corrupts character. Birds of a feather flock together. Whilst Owen and Peter may have had the same parents, if Owen's friends at school were more optimistic and Peter's friends pessimistic, it could lead to their characters being polarised.

Loneliness

Loneliness can also be a problem. People who have more secluded childhoods can potentially be more negative – as loneliness allows more time for introspection and negative rumination.

Response

We all have a choice how we respond to life's events. Even though the children may have had similar upbringings they may have responded differently to those events and these small choices over time can compound and polarise the two children. The father may have asked "Can you get to bed by 7pm" and Owen might have repeatedly been obedient, whilst Peter may have constantly been disobedient. Over time these choices may have changed their outlook on life. We always have a choice.

Age

Age difference and simply that one child is born first is a significant factor in the development of a child. When I was younger, I remember seeing my mother verbally telling off my brothers for walking too close to the kerb edge. My mother never had to tell me not to walk near the edge of the road. How did my oldest brother learn not to walk by the kerb? By being verbally reprimanded. How did I learn not to walk by the edge of the pavement? By fear of being reprimanded by my mother. I saw my brothers being told off, so I learnt from the example of my brothers. My eldest brother did not have an example to learn from. Potentially the youngest in families may learn more from example, from the mistakes of the older child, and out of fear of being reprimanded. The eldest may not have this factor, but being the firstborn they may have a higher level of risk and subsequently less fear.

Parenting Changes

The assumption that each child has an equal upbringing is far from the truth. Of course, a parent would find it difficult to accept that they've parented their children differently. Parents change their methods over time. Parents may be too harsh or too lax on their first child and alter their approach to the second. The parents themselves change. If the oldest child is parented when the father has a really stressful job but the younger child was parented when the father gets a less stressful job there may be knock-on effects to the child's development.

Input and the senses

What we see and listen to affects our minds. So we need to choose these wisely. Some psychologists have conducted various studies as to whether violent films and video games affect character and induce violent behaviour. The problem with these studies is that firstly, it is difficult to study these things in isolation, and secondly, how do you measure the effects over time?

When you grow things in the garden, you sow seeds. If you took a snapshot of the ground, planted a seed, then took another photo one week later there would be no significant difference and hence you might conclude that the seed made no difference. However, give it a year and there may be a significant difference.

What we watch, read and listen to is like sowing seeds into our subconscious. It may not have any immediate effect, but often there can be effects 2, 10, 20 years down the line. Of course, seed growth is also affected by the quality of the soil, air, light and water. The same seed may take longer to germinate in certain conditions.

Someone who watches a film who is sensitive will react immediately. This is similar to a seed being sown, instantly germinating and growing into a sapling. One of my previous housemates used to suffer bad nightmares after watching violent films. Other people may feel that violence doesn't affect them, and only to find that in years to come it has affected them much more subtly. It may be that the effect of what they had seen on television was simply lying dormant. The dormant seed germinated later which subsequently affected their thoughts and behaviour. We need to be careful what we watch and listen to, even if we feel it isn't affecting us in the present moment.

On a positive note, I also believe this happens to good things. Every time I listen to Mozart or hear a phrase like "Keep going, you are doing well" it may not immediately show any difference, but eventually positive input can radically affect your life. It's one of the principles of learning by osmosis.

As mentioned previously, if you are constantly listening to negative song lyrics, negative news, people arguing etc, it is like sowing negative seeds into your life. Those negative seeds will affect your future.

Peace / Mindfulness

Imagine you stand on a cliff near a beach and shut your eyes - what can you hear? Waves rolling in from the ocean, seagulls, the grass blowing in the gentle breeze, a cricket chirping, and a bee buzzing around. Now imagine you are still on the same cliff – what can you see? White fluffy clouds drifting by; little white crests rolling in from the ocean, forming waves and tumbling onto the sand; clover blowing in the wind and the occasional cricket jumping within the grass. Now imagine what you can feel? The warmth of the sun on your face and the soft grass in your hands.

The scenario above is an example of being mindful. If you were actually on that beach you might not have noticed all those sounds, feeling and sights because you might have been busy thinking about what to cook for supper. Those who are depressed might sit on the same beach and not hear anything apart from their depressing thoughts. We are not actually that good at listening to other things besides our own thoughts. So part of being relaxed is using your senses to become more aware of your surroundings.

Mindfulness is defined as an ability to concentrate on the present. The majority of our negative thoughts are fears about the future, and guilt, shame or regrets about the past. By constantly thinking about the past and future it can rob us of enjoying the present. Being aware of the present is key.

How many times has your mind wandered to negative thoughts that distract you from the present? When you start eating a bar of chocolate, you may notice the flavours, but by the time you get to the last bite you may not even be aware of the taste. When reading a book whilst tired, you read a page then realise you've taken none of it in, and need to re-read it.

To enjoy the present it is important to be aware of the different senses. What can you taste, smell, hear, see, and feel? Certain hobbies can help you to be more mindful. Photography can help you to be more aware of what you can see. Listening to music can help you be more mindful of the moment. Joining a cookery class may help you to develop more awareness of taste.

Whilst mindfulness is a useful tool, it should not be, however, used to ignore problems. We still need to use our memories of the past in order to develop thankfulness. And we need to project positive memories onto the future to produce hope.

In my experience and understanding there could be a danger with mindfulness. I believe that if we constantly practise living in the present, we are not using our memory. If we don't use our memory, just like a muscle, it may become weaker and therefore extreme amounts of mindfulness could lead to memory complications. There are some studies that suggest this is the case.

> "The same aspects of mindfulness that create countless benefits can also have the unintended negative consequence of increasing false-memory susceptibility."[38]

It's early stages when it comes to the science surrounding mindfulness. The length of time spent and the way it is implemented may all have an impact on mental health. Personally, I see mindfulness as being aware of your senses and what they are perceiving; not opening up a blank mind and clearing your thoughts – as practised in eastern religious meditation.

Use your senses to enjoy the world around you.

Stop and admire life around you.
There is more life around
you than you realise.

Procrastination

Various articles suggest that procrastination is an increasing problem in society.[39] How one measures that is beyond my understanding. However, it seems that more and more people put off making or acting on decisions. If we procrastinate it can make us low. Sadly we can end up in a cycle where we delay a decision, beat ourselves up, and then continue to delay. In *The Procrastination Equation* Dr Piers Steel tells us that procrastination is related to the following equation:

$$\text{Motivation} = \frac{\text{Expectancy} \times \text{Value}}{\text{Impulsiveness} \times \text{Delay}}$$

His theory states that to prevent procrastination we need motivation. Motivation comes from the following:

Expectancy

If we expect to fail, then our low expectancy will lead to procrastination. On the contrary, when we expect to succeed, we are driven to start as soon as possible. I agree with his understanding here. What is the solution? How do we start to expect a good result? Instilling hope and imagining success is key. The first step we can make towards imagining ourselves succeeding is to recognise we often imagine tasks incorrectly.

Have you ever put off a task only to realise it wasn't so bad once you had started?

The task you dread is probably not as half as bad as you think

One of the best ways we can expect a good result is to remember all the previous successes we've had and the successes of other people in similar circumstances. Success breeds success. Also, your expectancy is based on hope, so everything else in this book should contribute to helping you become motivated. Remember that in order to build a strong imagination we need to develop positive memories.

Value

Dr Steel suggests that "Value" is key to our motivation. For example, I find being motivated to pay a credit card bill fairly easy because I really don't want to pay the late fees. I value this highly. However, I don't highly value having neatly trimmed grass and therefore I will often procrastinate mowing the lawn. If you don't value something highly you may be subject to putting it off. However, what Dr Steel is missing here is that if you value something excessively high you may also end up putting it off.

270

Consider buying three items:

1. *Kettle descaler (low value)*
   I keep saying to myself, I'll get the kettle descaler tomorrow. I don't value it as highly important and therefore I keep putting it off or I simply forget about it when I go shopping.

2. *Bicycle pump (medium value)*
   My bicycle pump is working but it keeps leaking. I use my bike every day and therefore it is fairly important to me. The value means I am motivated to buy a new one, however, I'm not overly fussy about what a bike pump may look like as long as it functions. I have a balanced value of it, therefore the purchase happens quickly.

3. *A laptop (overvalued)*
   My laptop is slow and old. I've decided to buy a new laptop. I value it is as extremely important. Because I want to get the best I can for my money I keep looking on the internet and researching what to get. I keep delaying my decision because I overvalue what I want to buy. I want it to be the best laptop I can get. Perhaps I need to not value it so highly.

Notice that these are my valuations of what I am purchasing. Similarly, valuations could vary between people. Consider three people buying a bicycle:

1. *Jenny – the occasional cyclist (low valued bike)*
   Jenny occasionally uses her bike. It is old and she needs a new one. Because she doesn't value her bike and cycling that much she keeps putting off the decision of buying a bike.

2. *Kevin – the commuter (high valued bike)*
   Kevin commutes to work and therefore a bike is important and valued. He doesn't procrastinate making a decision. He goes to a few shops and chooses his favourite.

3. *Donald – the avid cyclist (overvalued bike)*
   Donald is an avid cyclist. He loves his bike; not only does he commute but he spends days cycling in the mountains at the weekends. He wants to get the best bike, he spends months researching on the internet what to buy, can't make up his mind, and even when he thinks he knows which one to buy he still puts off the decision. He procrastinates excessively because he values his bike so much – potentially overvaluing, even making an idol of his bike.

When we under-value something we are likely to put off making a decision, but also when we overvalue something we are likely to delay something.

**Procrastination can happen when we
make an idol out of something.**

Impulsiveness
Due to the many distractions in life we are more likely to put things off if we are impulsive. If you are in a locked cell with nothing else to do and there is an unwritten cheque on the floor and your task is to write a cheque, you are most likely to do it. If there are hundreds of other things to do, then impulsiveness tends to lead to procrastinating other tasks. For example, if you have the internet, you have hundreds of shops at your fingertips, games and other distractions to hand. Part of not procrastinating is not impulsively being distracted by these. Your physical location can have a huge impact on the distractions available. I have written most of this book whilst sipping a coffee at my local Waitrose, coffee shops and

libraries. These can be great places to work as there are fewer distractions than your own home. Where are you less distracted?

Delay
Dr Steel adds the idea of delay in the equation as to why we might procrastinate. If Christmas is tomorrow, we are much less likely to procrastinate choosing a Christmas present than if it is in ten weeks time. Because we don't tend to plan for the future we can end up delaying things to the last minute, so having a healthier view of the future will allow us to complete things sooner.

Whilst Dr Steels book is of great value I believe a few key ideas about procrastination are missed out of his equation so I shall touch on these here.

Guilt
When we procrastinate we can feel guilty for not getting on with the task. The great thing about completing the task now is that we will get rid of the guilty feeling earlier. Emmett's law states:

'The dread of doing a task uses up more time and energy than doing the task itself'

Fear
Fear is a major part of why we procrastinate. The fears that most commonly interfere with decision-making are:

- Fear of disappointment
- Fear of disapproval
- Fear of criticism
- Fear of uncertainty
- Fear of something better round the corner
- Fear of not getting the best

273

"**Fear of disappointment**" is a common reason to procrastinate. For example, If you are fearful when buying a new TV that you might make the wrong choice and be disappointed, you may delay making your decision.

Are you trying to protect yourself from disappointment by delaying the decision? You cannot prevent yourself from disappointment by delaying a decision. If the result is disappointing it is better to find out now. Making correct decisions 100% of the time is impossible; it is inevitable that you will make some bad decisions in life and find some results of your decisions disappointing.

> **You cannot prevent yourself from**
> **disappointment by delaying a decision.**
> **If the result is disappointing, it is better**
> **to find out now than later.**

Once I spent hours and hours researching which virtual string orchestra to buy for my computer. Eventually, I thought I'd bought the correct one, but discovered that certain aspects didn't live up to my expectations; yes some things disappointed me. I'd spent ages doing research which was, in hindsight, excessive. However, my lengthy research did not prevent me from feeling disappointed. In fact, if I'd discovered my disappointment with the software earlier, I would have been able to remedy the situation quicker.

Often procrastination can result from the "**Fear of disapproval and criticism**". For example, if you are fearful of someone criticising your choice of wallpaper, you may delay your decision. You probably imagine more criticism than you are likely to get. If it is invalid criticism then why do you need to fear it? If it is valid criticism then wouldn't it be better to know now than later?

"Fear of uncertainty" is similar to the fear of disappointment. You may be trying to choose a holiday in a sunny place. Perhaps you think that if you make the right choice you can guarantee not having rain. In your attempt to find this certainty you keep putting off decisions because you are never 100% sure. Nothing is certain and you cannot make anything certain by delaying a decision.

We all want to feel we are getting the best value for our money, choosing the best holiday, choosing the best present, or best job. However, the **"Fear of not getting the best"** and **"Fear of something better round the corner"** can cripple our decisions.

I remember when I used to go shoe shopping I used to visit every shoe shop in town looking at all the shoes before finally going back to the shop which had the nicest shoes. It's good that I didn't live in London at the time, otherwise I'd still be shoe shopping! There will always be something better round the corner.

What's more, it's not just about what is round the corner but, in addition, what will come out in the future. At the time of writing this section I was about to buy a virtual brass sample library for my computer. Just when I'd made a decision what to buy I heard about another company releasing a new virtual library. In such circumstances, what should I do? Should I wait to hear the new one? I could spend my life waiting for each new release, and there is almost certainly going to be something better released in the future.

> **If I want to get the best TV in the world,**
> **I should wait until one day before I die.**
> **But if I want to get the most out of a TV,**
> **I should buy one today.**

We often see missing out on the best as fatal. But not having the best isn't fatal; a bad choice is not necessarily a disaster. Often your decisions will be replaced in a couple of years time anyway. For example, the TV you buy will be gone in 5 years time and replaced by a different better one, so why get so uptight about this decision. You may learn something from making a bad decision, about yourself, the particular thing you are choosing, or learn how to make better decisions in the future.

Is a wrong choice so bad?

"I have not failed. I've just found 10,000 ways that won't work." *Thomas Edison*

"If I am not making any mistakes, I can be sure I am not learning and growing."[40]

Research

One of the other elements that Dr Steel has left off his equation is the amount of choice. If we are faced with a decision where there are only two choices, it will be much quicker to make a decision. If, however, we are faced with a huge amount of choice, the options can become daunting and, as a result, we can become paralysed by the decision-making and consequently end up procrastinating.

In order to make choices we often undertake research. However, sometimes the research can become obsessive, and, as a result, we delay in making a choice and procrastinate.

Is research paralysing your progression?
Are you doing too much research?

How much time should you spend researching a particular problem? How do we define a *reasonable* amount of time for research on any given problem. Is spending 30 hours on the internet researching what shower curtain to buy acceptable? Is 30 hours surfing the internet to buy a computer acceptable?

How reusable is the research that you are doing? If I spend two months looking at which camera to buy, the research itself will become dated. In another five years time when I come to buy a new camera I will need to undertake the research all over again because my findings will be out of date. If I now decide that the mid-range Nikon camera is the best, in 5 years time the Nikon cameras might not be. The features and specifications will have drastically changed and therefore my current research cannot be reused. It might be that the competition will have overtaken leaving Nikon cameras in the shadows.

Some other types of research, however, are longer lasting. For example, if I was researching what herb tastes best with tomato soup, and if I decide that oregano is the best combination, I will be able to use that finding time and time again.

Can I recycle my research or is this temporary research?

Don't forget that your life in itself is research. The decision you are making is already based on what you know about yourself, your likes and beliefs. For example, I already know that I would not want to buy a purple laptop, I would prefer black or white. See your research as adding to what you already know rather than starting from scratch. Why is your life's research not sufficient? Why do you need to do more?

My life is already research, why do I need to do more?

One of the reasons that people feel they need to undertake lots of research is because of fear. Sometimes people believe that the quality of a decision is based on the quality of their research. This is not true. Have you ever spent hours researching a decision only to then make the wrong decision, be disappointed and regret making that choice? Have you ever made a split-second decision, with little research, and yet been happy with your decision? Most likely these ring true for you.

When I bought my Toyota I didn't spend ages researching what to buy, and I am pleased with the purchase I made. On the other hand, I once spent ages researching some computer software to buy, and now I hardly ever use it because I was disappointed with its functionality.

My good research will not necessarily protect me from making a bad decision

Are you putting too much faith in your research? What is a reasonable amount of research? When does it become obsessive?

Too much research can clutter your thinking

Sometimes we undertake research and settle on a decision and then continue to research the answer. This is clearly rather pointless. Susie shops all over town for shoes. She visits 15 shops and decides that the red pair of shoes in John Lewis are the best. However, for the next week she continues to visit all the same shops trying to reassure herself that her decision was the best. Why do we continue to research when we have already made up our minds? It is probably because we don't trust our own research. So how can we start to trust our own research?

Here are some points that may help you to discover if your research is excessive:

- Can you reuse your research?

- Are you doing something new? Have you considered there is a learning curve?

- Are you over or under confident?

- Does your research need to be done now? Could you park it and come back afresh?

- Do you have too much time for research?

- Have you given yourself too little time for research?

- Are you over-valuing your research?

- What do you expect your research to achieve?

- Is your research based on fear?

- Is there a better way to do this research?

- Can you allocate the research to someone else?

- Will your research make a noticeable difference?

- If you do too much research will you be faced with too many options later on?

- How do others perceive your research?

- How will research benefit your character?

- Are you continuing to do research when you have already made up your mind?

- Have you done the task before?

- Are you looking for one solution to fit every scenario?

- Are you looking for one shoe to fit every occasion?

One interesting thing to remember is that there is no such thing as perfect research and a perfect solution. For instance, you may be looking for a car that is comfortable, fast, looks good, extremely economical, has lots of boot space, can take 5 passengers, is customisable, and doesn't cost much to buy. A Ferrari with five passengers, for less than £15k, that is fast and does 45 miles to the gallon.

I'm sorry it doesn't exist. It is similar with lots of our choices. If you are looking for one shoe that will cater for all your needs, you are going to spend your life living in frustration. There is no perfect solution. What are the most important aspects? Which solution meets those aspects the most?

There is no shoe that can fit every occasion.

Joseph is researching how to paint in the style of Renoir. In the first 60 days of his research he finds out 90% of the technique he needs to use in order to paint like Renoir. He continues his research for another 60 days but his findings are similar and his research has only progressed by 2% creeping up to 92%.

His research is inverse proportional as it takes increasingly more effort to get more out of his research. It's like squeezing an orange; 90% comes out with little effort, but to get the last 10% out it takes increasingly more effort.

Joseph realises that it is futile spending another 60 days to get from 92% to 93%, he realises his continued research is not adding huge value to his decisions and skill level. He realises that his mind is becoming cluttered with research. Yet despite all this he finds it hard to stop his research. He wants to get to 100% and so- called "complete" his research. He is stuck and wants to move forward, realises the futility of continued study but still wants to do it. What should we suggest? A friend suggested the following:

The best painters seem to know when to let a painting go rather than trying to endlessly correct "faults". Art has to be "right" but if we don't have the capacity to get it all right, we need to know when to stop trying, and capitalise on all the good work we have done.

Of course, this begs the question: what is "right"? Joseph needs to sit down and assess his priorities. What does it mean to him for a painting to be "right"? What are his criteria? I would suggest walking away and parking a project and asking these questions. If Joseph does something else for two months, when he comes back to the Renoir project he will most likely say "Oh yes. I think this is actually finished. It meets my criteria. I'm happy to move on".

Joseph also needs to consider if there are more important projects he should be embarking on. What Joseph needs to do is to start by writing down all his other dreams and ambitions. As he focuses more on those, his Renoir project will become less important. Joseph isn't going to find much relief in saying "I must stop working on this Renoir project". He will more likely find relief by saying "Let's start working on this new project".

If you are having difficulty finishing a project, assess your completion criteria, walk away, start on a new task, and then come back later.

Perception of Procrastination
Your perception of procrastination will drastically change the amount of time you take to make a decision. What you feel might be excessive procrastination may be being hard on yourself, similarly what you may consider research may indeed be excessive and a form of procrastination.

Gerald is given 1 task at work. The task will take 10 days to complete. Boris, on the other hand, is given 5 tasks that will each take 2 days to complete. A similar total of 10 days.

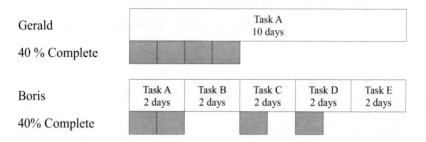

After day four Boris has spent two days on task A, one day on task C, and one day on task D. Because he hasn't started on tasks B or E he feels like he is procrastinating. However, those feelings arise because he is neglecting other tasks. Boris is working just as hard as Gerald. He just has more tasks.

The more plates you have to spin the more you will feel you are procrastinating with those tasks. Don't beat yourself up, you may just have a lot of things going on.

Sometimes we can get stuck on the detail when the detail is not important now. When an artist paints a portrait he starts by sketching the overall shape of a head. He then will fill in the detail later on. If he started by filling in the detail of each face part before completing the overall shape of the head, there is a likelihood that he might have to redo it. Also, he will feel as though he isn't making huge amounts of progress.

Start with the broad strokes and finesse later

Procrastination can also come from our perception of measuring time. Tasks will often take considerably longer than we expect. For example, you start the ironing and expect it to last one hour before cutting the grass. If two hours later you are still doing the ironing, there can be a tendency to feel you are putting off or delaying cutting the grass. In this instance we know you are not putting off cutting the grass because you don't value it, but simply because you underestimated how long it would take to do the ironing.

> **Procrastination can result from poor time management and the underestimation of how long other tasks take to complete.**

For this reason we need to come up with realistic deadlines and estimate task completion times correctly. Doing so may be challenging. How can you become better at setting yourself realistic deadlines? Are you giving yourself enough contingency for unexpected interruptions?

You also need to consider these questions when working with others. Even if your deadlines are realistic for you, they may not be realistic for others. Likewise, a deadline may be realistic for others but not for you.

A lack of knowledge in any area will lead to us underestimating the time it takes to do something. You may think that writing a book is fairly easy if you've never done one. You may think that authors write books in a couple of weeks, when in reality it takes months or years. Be careful that you don't accuse others of being slow or procrastinating when it is simply your lack of understanding of how long it takes to do something.

Too much time
Procrastination can also occur due to having too much time. There is an old saying:

> **"Work expands to fill the time available"[41]**

283

If you give yourself too much time, there are two potential problems. If a task realistically takes 5 hours, and you give yourself 10 hours, you may end up spending 10 hours doing it. This might not seem like procrastination, but if you have other tasks to complete, then it has delayed those tasks and you will feel like you are procrastinating on them.

Alternatively, if you give yourself 10 hours to complete a 5 hour task, you may find you don't start it until 3 hours before the deadline. It is better to divide your time up into segments.

For example, Janet has to shop for a present for her friend. She reckons it will take 2 hours. She also has a huge amount of ironing to do that she predicts will also take 2 hours. If she thinks "I have 4 hours to complete the ironing and shopping", that will mentally lead to more procrastination than if she thinks, "I have 2 hours to do the shopping and 2 hours to complete the ironing".

Break your deadlines and time estimations into smaller sizes. It makes them seem more immediate.

Clarity

Another element that is not mentioned in Dr Steel's book is "clarity". In order to be motivated it is important to know what you are heading towards. For example, if you told me that there was a party at the weekend but didn't tell me the day, time, or where it was, it would be difficult to get motivated and excited about going to the party.

In order to gain clarity we need to do some research into the details. Can you come up with a strategy? Can you write down the pros and cons of the options available? As things come into focus we will either become more attracted or less attracted to the options available.

It's easier to aim for a target when it is in focus

Roadblocks

You are faced with a major decision, you are at a road junction and not sure which way to go. One way is best and correct but you are not sure which one.

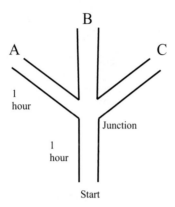

Doris takes one hour to get from the start to the junction, then she is faced with a decision. Which way should she go? Let's say that C is the best direction but she doesn't know that. She spends 1 hour doing research, but she is unsure which road to take so she sits there for a further 11 hours trying to decide. Finally she makes a decision. The total time she takes to get from the start to C is:

Start to Junction	1 hour
Research at the Junction	1 hour
Further research and procrastination	11 hours
Travel from the Junction to C	1 hour
Total time to get from Start to C	**14 hours**

In comparison, Lorna takes one hour to get from the start to the junction, then she is faced with a decision. Which way should she go? Let's say that C is still the best direction but she doesn't know that. She spends 1 hour doing research, but she is unsure. She takes a leap of faith and heads towards A. She gets to A and realises she's made a mistake. She makes her way back to the junction. She then decides to go to for option B. She travels up to B but again realises she has made a mistake, so comes back to the junction and travels up to C. The total time she takes to get from the start to C is:

Start to Junction	1 hour
Research at the Junction	1 hour
Travel to A and back to the Junction. (She made a mistake)	2 hours
Travel to B and back to the Junction. (She made a mistake)	2 hours
Travel from the Junction to C	1 hour
Total time to get from Start to C	**7 hours**

Despite Lorna making bad mistakes she actually got from the start to the finish quicker than Doris. Also, Lorna learnt a lot more about options A and B than Doris did. Lorna will also feel much more confident about her final decision, Doris may still doubt her decision. Lorna will have also enjoyed more roads and the lack of stress being stuck at the junction.

Some wisdom is required here. Obviously, with exploring different roads there is not a huge cost involved apart from time. You might be able to take a similar attitude with finding a career. If you spend 10 years trying to figure out which career to pursue, you might have, in the same time, completed three short term contracts or work experience in different fields. Taking the same approach to dating might be more problematic. "Well I'm not sure which girl to date" so I'll try option A and if it doesn't work out try option B. Also, it depends on how long each road is. The analogy is not bulletproof, but the main concept is summarised as follows:

It may be better, and less costly, to explore than procrastinate. Going up the wrong road may be less drastic than being stuck at the junction.

By the time you've spent 4 hours at the fork in the road, you could have spent 4 hours going up one road and back up the other road.

On a positive note, if you are procrastinating, realise that you are half-way to your goal. At least you are not stuck at the start. It is better to be stuck half-way along the road and be thankful for what you have already achieved than be still at the start. You can't put off plans you haven't made, so you must have made a least some plan. Pat yourself on the back for having made a plan.

Make time to make a decision

People who are pressed for time will, most likely, continue to use the same methods for decision-making. Those methods might not be the most time efficient, and might not give them the best results. Sometimes it is better to take some time out to consider your options and analyse the way you are making decisions.

Busy people might not be completing tasks in the most efficient manner, or reaping the best results. So make some time to stop and consider your life.

Accountability

People sometimes say "I don't want to be accountable to anyone". Accountability is often seen as negative and limiting freedom, but accountability is actually very useful. At school children often have to be accountable for their actions. I had a variety of teachers: some would meticulously check homework, to see if it had been completed and that it had been done properly, and other teachers would give homework and then not even check if it was completed. Without accountability for my homework I could have got away without doing it. The significance of homework was to encourage progress. With accountability I could progress quicker; without accountability my progress could have been hindered. Instead of seeing accountability as a negative thing which prevents freedom, we should see it as a positive force in our lives.

Accountability promotes progress

Accountability can be both voluntary or involuntary:

Voluntary Accountability

A dietician asks a client "What have you eaten this week?"; this requires a voluntary honest response. Without the honesty, the accountability isn't going to be effective.

Involuntary Accountability

A mother installs an app to monitor her daughter's use of the internet. The daughter is automatically accountable to the mother if she visits any websites the mother disapproves of. This type of accountability can seem harsh, but it can also be effective in making progress.

Voluntary and involuntary accountability will be useful in certain contexts. The aim of accountability is twofold. Firstly, to prevent negative consequences, and secondly and ideally, to change our desires.

Prevention and Change:

Being accountable can prevent us from making mistakes or doing things that we don't want to do. If a child knows that their mother is monitoring their internet usage, that may stop them from visiting certain websites. Similarly, if we see a dietician every week and report to them what we have eaten it may prevent us from eating that piece of cake we see in the coffee shop. Does it change the desire to eat the piece of cake? It can do. But to understand this we need to consider long-term and short term desire – often referred to as impulsiveness.

An example of accountability in my own life is when I was trying to eat more healthily. I was trying to give up eating cheese. In the long-term my desire was "to give up eating cheese". However, despite my long-term goal to give up cheese, I would still experience temporary impulsive desires to eat cheese. This is where accountability came in handy. The awareness of accountability would suppress my short term impulsive desires.

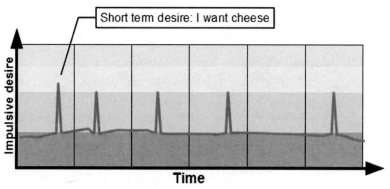

Long term desire: give up cheese

Note that to begin with the impulsive short term desires are contrary to the long-term desire: "I want to eat cheese now" versus "I want to give up cheese long-term". The accountability, however, will often stop us acting on those short term desires and prevent us from the consequences. I presume the reason why accountability is so effective is that our need to be accepted and approved of by others is so strong that it can override our short-term impulses.

Strength of short term impulses may decrease

At the of a period of accountability the short term impulses are strong. However, the more we resist, the weaker those impulses will become.

"I want to have cheese" was a strong impulsive desire at the start. But after six weeks of accountability, my actual desire for cheese lessened. Not only did the impulses weaken, but the frequencies of those impulses also diminished. Now I don't really have a strong desire to eat cheese at all; in fact I could happily live without it. In this example of accountability my actual desire for cheese changed over time. I presume that this is because as we give up habits our brain structure changes and this affects the desire. My longer-term goal was reached here. However, this might not always be the case.

Impulse doesn't change – but consequences do.

Let's say in the previous example, my desire for cheese over the long-term didn't change. Let's also say that the short term impulses also remained the same in intensity and frequency. You may think in this case that accountability is a waste of time. Each time you are tempted to eat cheese the accountability frustrates you: "I really want to eat cheese – I can't – I need to resist". Of course that frustration is not good. Ideally, you want the accountability to actually change your long-term desires. However, even if it doesn't change your desires, and even if you are frustrated by accountability – it doesn't mean the accountability is of little use. Accountability still prevents negative consequences. In this instance, it would stop you eating cheese and subsequently putting on weight.

**Accountability prevents acting on
short term impulsiveness**

**Accountability prevents consequences
of short term impulsiveness**

Accountability to others:
As seen in my cheese example, being accountable can actually change our desires. Accountability can be used in all areas of life. In theory it should be possible to be accountable to yourself, but I find this less effective than being accountable to someone else. Ideally, we want to be accountable to others. As we grow older we tend to have fewer people to be accountable to; maybe that is why we make less progress.

Accountability brings change

"As iron sharpens iron, so one person sharpens another" *Solomon*

Of course, if we are to be accountable to others attitude is vital. Honesty is important. Never lie; this is corrosive and defeats the purpose of accountability. If I am accountable to someone about how much exercise I do each week, then if I lie, I will never achieve the long-term goal. Keep telling yourself that accountability and honesty promote progress.

If you are lacking motivation in an area and want to see progress and change, then consider how you might introduce accountability. The following are some ideas:

- Install an accountability app on your phone and be accountable to someone for how much time you are spending on certain apps.

- Meet someone once a week and show them your food and exercise diary.

- Ask your boss to give you regular appraisals.

- Regularly meet with a friend to discuss your life-goals, the steps you need to take, and your progress with each of these steps.

- Ask your friends to point out any negative language you use. See page 140.

Summary

- Anger directed at oneself turns into depression. We get angry when goals are blocked and when we feel we've wasted time or resource. When we focus out we diminish our chances of becoming angry.

- Decision-making is difficult because we are blessed with so much choice. Our choices shape our future, but even bad choices can be turned around for good. Don't let a bad decision define you, learn something from it.

- Envy steals hope. Envy often results from not knowing your destiny and is rooted in the present. Find your true identity and reconsider your desires within the grand scheme of things.

- Fear is in your imagination and therefore memories. Everything you've ever wanted is on the other side of fear. We need to replace fear with courage and love. Take a risk – what's the worst that can happen?

- Disappointment can be prevention.

- Scepticism can rob us of hope. If we question everything, we'll end up being emotionally paralysed and waste a lot of time. Sometimes we have to trust.

- Guilt and shame are corrosive. Open up to others about your thoughts and feelings.

- Nostalgia can be deceptive. Enjoy the present. Besides, you're never to old to start something new.

- Self-pity won't solve your issues. It is also not the best way to gain acceptance. Start noticing the people who do accept you and thanking them.

- Forgiveness is key to finding hope. True forgiveness is about creating new positive memory associations.

- Thankfulness generates hope. Every day presents an opportunity to increase your list of things to be thankful for.

- Perfectionism is about imbalanced priorities and poor time management. Don't try harder, try different.

- Control is about understanding your level of responsibility. We can't control the world; but we can control our reactions to it.

- Self-esteem is important. We are all looking for Significance, Acceptance and Security. We need to examine how we measure these. You are significant simply because you are you. Don't focus on rejection, focus on the people who do accept you. Security is not about having things; it's about handling things, and building healthy relationships.

- Peace will flow when we use our senses to enjoy the world around us.

- Procrastination is often based on how highly we value something. Sometimes the dread of doing a task uses up more time and energy than doing the task itself.

- Accountability promotes progress – so find friends who you can be accountable to.

Change your thinking - Part 4
Circumstantial Thinking

Earlier in the book we discussed changing your circumstances; here we talk about changing your thoughts within those circumstances. Your life can be divided into the following areas:

Life areas
Money, Friendships, Family, Loneliness, Partner, Addictions, Physical Health, Mental Health, Spiritual Health, Hobbies, Sport, Work, Tastes, Character.

Tastes

A lot of people may end up in a career without thinking about it. They may end up doing a job because their family encouraged them, or their school teacher had an influence on them. Sometimes people are misled into doing jobs and haven't stopped to think, "Why am I doing this"? I also believe this is true when it comes to "What people like". People think they like something, but if they stopped to truly consider why they like it, they may find it difficult to answer those questions. They may simply like something because it was projected onto them as a child.

Do you know – truly know what you like? Why?

You may find that your preferences and likes in life have been involuntarily forced upon you. At school you may have been teased every time you had a particular type of haircut and, as a result, started to dislike that haircut. Or you may have seen short girls being teased for being short and, as a result, formed a like of tall girls.

Jeremy used to dislike runny honey when he was younger simply because his brother, when lifting his knife out, would let the honey spill over the side. When Jeremy was passed the jar it was sticky. Jeremy's reason for not liking honey was based on the jar being sticky. Now Jeremy is a bachelor and he is the only person who uses the honey jar; he doesn't have to drip honey down the side of the jar – he can keep his jar dry and clean. Consequently, he now likes the taste of honey because the negative association of "I'll get sticky hands" has been removed.

When people form likes they can often become closed minded or fearful of leaving the familiar. You discover a new flavour of ice-cream. You try to offer it to a friend but they've already concluded that they don't like it before even tasting it. Is that familiar? Even if that person goes ahead and tries it they probably won't like it. That is because their mind has already informed their taste buds that this is a flavour they don't like. This psychological behaviour is fairly common in children and I seem to remember a few instances where I had a similar attitude. By being closed minded we can miss discovering what we truly like.

**Don't be fearful of leaving the familiar.
Try something out before turning your nose up.**

It is also important to give adequate time to assess something.

Jill has been to the same cafe for years, eaten the same cake and drunk the same type of coffee. Sadly the shop she likes closes for refurbishment. She enters a different shop and decides the coffee and cake taste terrible. However, over time she actually starts to realise she prefers this new coffee shop. She meets new staff who are more pleasant; she discovers a new cake and she acquires a taste for the coffee. After some time the old coffee shop reopens and she returns to discover that actually she prefers her new shop.

**We need time to find out what we truly like
in life, to be open-minded, and to try.**

Socialising, Rejection and Loneliness

Sometimes we feel that we should be able to solve our depression problems on our own. To a certain extent I have had an isolated lonely life, but I must acknowledge that reading books (which I feel is like crawling into someone else's mind for a while), friends and family have been paramount in overcoming depression. Often we think we should be able to find solutions on our own. This is tragic because we were never meant to live alone, we were designed for community.

One of the dangers of being depressed is that you feel you can't socialise, that you don't want to socialise and should stay on your own until you can deal with your problems. When you imagine socialising perhaps you think some of the following thoughts:

- I don't have the energy to socialise.

- I won't be good company. What will others think of me?

- I won't know what to talk about.

- I need to sort out my problems first.

- I need to avoid alcohol and spending money.

Firstly, how much energy does it take to socialise? If you can sit on a sofa and have the energy to watch TV, do you not think it takes the same amount of energy to socialise sitting round a table in a pub? In reality, you probably spend more energy ruminating on your own than socialising. When we are on our own we have a tendency to ruminate on negative thoughts, so by staying on your own you are allowing the rumination to continue. Forcing yourself to socialise can be one of the best ways to break negative rumination as it is much more difficult to listen to your own thoughts when you are in the company of others.

Rumination on your own requires more energy than socialising

People want your company
Depression can often make us feel that we won't be good company. Why do you think that? It's because when we are depressed we don't like the company of our thoughts. However, your friends do not hear all your thoughts. Why do you think they asked you to socialise in the first place? It's because they enjoy your company. We can spend a lot of time guessing what others think of us, but in reality our conclusions are often not true. If in doubt you can always ask them; people admire honesty. Asking for feedback can be useful.

Your mental picture of socialising is more extreme than the reality.

It doesn't take as much energy as you may think.

You may jump to the false conclusion that others will not enjoy your company.

Remember, you are unique. You have a history, a combination of knowledge, and memories that no other person on the planet has. You are valuable to every conversation and social setting. You may also find that other people in your social setting also suffer with depression and by being honest, you may find someone to share and discuss problems with.

Conversation

You may find that, because your thoughts have been stuck like a record player, you fear what to talk about in social settings. You are not alone. Even people who don't suffer with depression can sometimes fear conversation. Have you ever been in a social setting where someone didn't speak? What did you think of them? You probably didn't think they were a failure for not speaking, so why would they think differently of you? You shouldn't feel pressure to make conversation. Nonetheless, others want to hear your views and ideas, you have a lot to offer, so here are some suggestions for conversations:

- Ask questions so that the other person is doing most of the speaking.

- Make observations and comments e.g. I like the way they've laid out the room.

- Find something in common.

- Keep to light-hearted topics such as the cinema, TV, food, holidays.

- Ask people what their favourites are. e.g. What is your favourite drink?

- Do some research. For example if you are going to a cake baking party you could read some cake recipes and magazines so that you have something to talk about when you arrive.

- Prepare what you will say. I don't mean verbatim, but if you are going to a discussion group you may want to write down some things that you want to raise.

Note that conversation takes practice, and that nearly all of us can improve our conversational skills. It is an interesting task to consider how you would start and maintain a conversation in various circumstances; as you practise these types of scenarios in your imagination, you can become more confident at improvising in real settings. The following is a difficult exercise, but it is excellent practice for your imagination.

- If someone in a queue at a coffee shop turned to you and said what a lovely day it was outside, how would you continue that conversation apart from saying a simple "Yes, it is."?

- If you were at a restaurant and the tables were so busy that you had to share one, how would you start a conversation and what would you choose to talk about?

- If your car broke down and you had to call out a tow truck, what would you talk about with the driver of the recovery vehicle?

- If you joined a choir and there was a tea break, what would you talk about to the other members of the group?

- How would you start a conversation with a complete stranger on the street?

Don't wait until you're ready

If I waited until I felt ready to write this book I would never have started. It is true of so many things in life. Public speakers never feel ready; musicians and actors always want a few more days rehearsing. Our feelings follow our actions.

Socialise despite your feelings.
If you wait until you feel ready,
you'll never start.

Avoiding alcohol

Another reason we can tend to avoid socialising is that we feel we want to avoid alcohol; we are worried we might not be able to resist the temptation, we simply want to avoid it because it is a depressant, or we are scared of spending too much money. Certainly it is advisable to avoid alcohol and being wise with our money is important. However, if we are avoiding socialising for these reasons, that is not good. Some suggestions are as follows:

- Tell your friends that you want to avoid drinking alcohol, that you don't want to buy drink rounds and ask if they could be a bit compassionate in that area. Most people will think you are brave, not weak, for suggesting such ideas. If you find it difficult to muster up the strength to say that, then you might do it via text or ask someone to act on your behalf. If your friends don't respect that choice, it may be worth considering who your true friends are and finding new ones.
- Avoid taking money with you to social events.
- Only take a little cash with you and no card.
- Join a social group where these pressures are not felt e.g. a choir, tennis club etc.

Rejection

If we feel rejected it can steal hope; however, we often jump to false conclusions. We might assume that because someone has not turned up to a party they must be rejecting us as a person. It is important to seek out the other side of the story.

> Janet offers Kieran a cup of coffee, but Kieran already has a cup and refuses. Janet doesn't realise he has one, so she reads this as rejection, that Kieran doesn't like her.

This mistake may seem obvious but sometimes we make similar mistakes. Often rejection is more imagined than real. If you are fearful of rejection, one of the best things you can do is take social risks more frequently. Also, realise that there will be some people who might reject you but it is better knowing sooner than later, and for every person that rejects you there are another ten people around the corner willing to accept you.

Often people reject each other because of disagreements. This is childish because if you rejected everyone you disagreed with you'd soon alienate the whole world. Nobody will have identical opinions to yourself because you are unique.

**If you "unfriend" a person because
you disagree, you'll eventually
alienate the whole world.**

You may be passionate about your opinions, but trying to convince others is sometimes difficult and sometimes you just have to let go.

Remember that the memory is crucial to building hope. If I remember all the times when people have rejected me, I will be full of fear of rejection. I need to take note and remember all the times that people have accepted me, and recall those memories as often as possible.

Family

Sometimes parents who feel they have lost their hope for life can end up transferring their aspirations and dreams onto their children. I was once in the swimming pool and encountered a mother who was trying to force her five year old daughter to swim sixty lengths. Why? Perhaps _she_ had always wanted to become an Olympic swimmer and felt as though she failed – now she was trying to force _her daughter_ to become an Olympic swimmer.

301

When hopes fail there can be a tendency to transfer personal ambitions onto children. This particular parent may now imagine her daughter winning a medal. Sadly this means all the mother's hope, dreams and ambitions are focused on the child. This is extremely unhealthy. By putting too much hope in your children to succeed and depending on your child for a sense of significance, acceptance and security you are heading towards a disaster zone. This is in effect idolising your child. Your child is not you. What if that mother puts all her hopes on her daughter winning a gold medal in the Olympics and it never happens? She will spiral into depression; guilt, shame, and thoughts of being an inadequate parent will overwhelm her.

It's extremely unhealthy to pin all your hopes on your children

Parents want the best for their children, but what is best for you may not be what is best for your children. Your love and nurture should be based on helping them find hope for themselves, not superimposing your own hopes and dreams onto them.

Parents who put too much hope or focus too much on their children can do this to the extent of damaging other relationships.

I remember when I was a child and my mother was talking to my father. If I interrupted and asked, "Where is the Lego?" my mother might say "One minute, I am talking to your father. Don't interrupt." This I believe was a good thing. Firstly, it taught me the politeness of waiting, and not interrupting. Secondly, it taught me that I was not the centre of the universe. And lastly it sent messages to my father that he was valued.

Since then I have encountered situations which are quite the opposite. I've been talking to a parent and a child has come up and asked a question such as "Where is the Lego?" The parent has then broken off all conversation with myself and gone upstairs to help the child find the Lego. What does this communicate? Firstly, it doesn't teach the child patience; secondly, it doesn't teach the child that his will may be crossed, and so it enhances selfishness. What's more, the parent sends signals to me that my conversation is of little relative importance, that she doesn't value my conversation. Of course, it is all about priorities. If a child ran up to a mother with a bleeding finger, then there is a priority over the conversation. However, it does seem a common trend that children's wants, not needs, are being over-prioritised, that parents have a tendency to idolise their children. I think one of the main reasons for this is that parents are potentially superimposing their own hopes onto their children.

Work

The majority of people spend a third of their life working; eight hours a day. Therefore, the way they think at work is critical.

Firstly, what is work? The recent definition of work today seems to be "If you are not sitting at your desk you are not working. If you don't work from 9-5 you're lazy." If you study the lives of some creative geniuses, you will find out that their concept of work and hours is unusual. Sometimes when you've got a problem that you are finding difficult to solve, the best thing you can do is have a rest or go for a walk. Some of my best ideas and solutions have come to me whilst walking. Beethoven, Goethe, Dickens, and Steve Jobs all used to walk regularly. Mark Zuckerberg, the creator of Facebook, holds some of his meetings whilst walking. Presumably he and a client will take a walk and note down valuable points on a Dictaphone.

"Solvitur Ambulando" is a Latin term which means "Solved whilst walking."

If you got up from your desk and told your boss you were going for a fifteen minute walk, you'd probably get a strange look or be told to get back to work. Even if you paced up and down in the same room you might be told to sit down. However, you might actually be more productive and come up with better ideas whilst walking. Walking actually stimulates the brain cells and in particular the hippocampus part of the brain which is crucial for memory, and subsequently hope and imagination. What can we learn from this:

Don't beat yourself up just because you are not sitting at a desk.

In the current culture we are hour obsessed, and rather time obsessed. Sadly companies choose to keep very proscriptive hours for pay. How many bosses would be willing to say, "Okay, we need to come up with a solution to this problem – let's all take a fifteen minute walk round the block and discuss ideas." That actually might increase productivity and creativity in the office.

Walk away and come back later. Don't get stuck.

It is also important to take enough breaks. Studies have shown that people who work from 9-5 with one hour for lunch are actually much more productive than those who work from 9-5 flat out.[42] Even though the former work one hour less, their attention span, efficiency and productivity are increased compared to the latter. Don't believe the lie that "If I work harder I will achieve more." To a certain extent it is true, but remember work is not sitting at a desk; that efficiency, attention span and methods make more of a difference than simply putting in more hours.

Working is not about the hours you put in, it's about the efficiency of your time.

There is a suggestion that our brains work at maximum efficiency for about 4 hours, generally this is between the hours of 10am and 2pm.[43]

For work and socialising it is important to schedule your time otherwise you may find it is easily wasted. Schedules help you to know where you are going, and allow you to focus on the current task without worrying about all the other things you need to complete.

If we work too hard we can end up with burnout. One of the most common characteristics of burnout is the lack of hope. It is important, therefore, to keep feeding our mind with positive memories and spend time in the mental gym.

The working environment seems to be increasingly pressurised. It is ironic that we have more and more time, more and more conveniences, and faster technology, and yet most companies want your task completed by yesterday. A good employer should consider the mental well-being of his/her employees but seldom this is seldom the case.

Firstly, if you are facing considerable stress from your boss, you should talk to him/her and tell him/her what you are struggling with. If he/she fails to make arrangements for you then you can always sign off sick. If you are severely stressed a doctor can write a sick note as evidence of your stress; legally an employer cannot sack you or force you to work due to sickness.

Talk to your boss if you have issues. Don't hide away.

Sometimes we find that we have many tasks at hand and we have to multitask. If you have many plates to spin it may be overwhelming. Therefore, it is important to prioritise the tasks and work out a schedule for your work. If you try to focus on all the plates at once, you'll end up taking your eyes off the plate you are spinning and drop it. So it's good to concentrate on the task at hand.

**Don't focus on all the plates you are
trying to spin, otherwise you'll drop
the plate you're spinning.**

Prioritising work can be difficult. If you have a boss to ask, then that can be one of the most useful ways to prioritise. However, if not, you could consider the following:

If you have ten easy tasks and three difficult tasks you could either:

1. Do the easy jobs first. Once you've done those, you can tick off your progress and that will make you feel positive. "I've done 10/13 tasks. Great!" That will give you hope to do the other three. However, also be aware that you need to leave enough time for the last three.

2. Do the difficult jobs first. Once you have completed them, you'll have a sense of relief – that it is an easy ride downhill from now on.

3. Start with a few easy tasks to ease you in. Then do the difficult tasks. Finish with the rest of the easy tasks.

In any given circumstance try out these different strategies. You'll probably find that certain strategies suit your temperament better than others.

Sometimes prioritising is about saying "No". It may be hard to pluck up the courage to say no, but the pain of plucking up courage and saying "No" may be less than the pain you have to go through for saying yes and completing what you've been asked to do.

Money and Fame

True hope doesn't disappoint us. If your life is chasing a false hope you may momentarily experience joy but eventually disappointment will strike you. Hope deferred makes the heart sick. Why is it that so many people want to be famous?

Spending your life hoping to become famous is a recipe for depression. There is no guarantee you'll be famous. If you pin your hopes on becoming famous, you may spend the rest of your life constantly disappointed. Besides, fame is not a permanent state. You could be famous now but not tomorrow.

Deep down the three things we are looking for in life are Significance, Acceptance and Security. People believe that by becoming famous they can deeply fulfil these areas, that if they're famous they will feel more accepted, feel more significant, and have a bank balance to feel more secure. Ultimately, being rich or famous cannot fulfil these needs.

Robin Williams was extremely significant in the world of comedy, accepted by many and financially secure. However, did he feel it?

> "I used to think that the worst thing in life was to end up alone. It's not. The worst thing in life is to end up with people who make you feel alone."
> *Robin Williams*

Deep down even if you are accepted by others, you also need to be able to accept yourself. Money doesn't equal security, and we shouldn't measure success and significance by how popular we are. Besides, what a lot of people forget is that:

With great privilege comes great responsibility

One of the biggest problems with being rich or famous is that people are attracted to all the privileges but completely forget all the costs and responsibilities.

Some of the responsibilities of being rich or famous are:

- Being a role model to young people
- Behaving well at all times – people are watching you
- Using your money responsibly
- The more you have, the more you have to maintain

Some of the costs of being rich or famous are:

- Having potential paparazzi follow you round
- Invasion of privacy
- Criticism
- Rumours
- Constant travel
- Stalkers
- You can become a greater target for criminals
- Trust issues – people may be your friends because of your money rather than simply because they love you
- Dating issues – people may want to marry you for all the wrong reasons
- Marital issues – can your partner cope with the limelight?
- Reputation is at stake – put one foot wrong and you could be all over the tabloids
- Increased pressures i.e. more stress at work or more demands on your time
- You may find it difficult to go for a local walk

- You may find it difficult to go to a local restaurant
- You might not be able to take a holiday whenever you want to
- Your diary may end up so full that you don't have the time to spend the money you've earned and enjoy your life

Hoping to be rich or famous could lead to a lot of disappointment and depression. Not everyone can be rich and famous. It is preferable to pin your hopes on something else. A lot of celebrities have become famous and rich as a result of what they do, not because they were aiming to be rich and famous in the first place. Authors are not normally rich from trying to be rich, but from trying to write good books.

Sexual problems

Sexual problems can lead to a lack of hope; sometimes they are complex. A sexual problem could include the following:

- Feeling sexually frustrated.
- Being addicted to pornography.
- Binging on sex.
- Constantly fantasising about sex.
- Being unfaithful to partners.
- Being addicted to masturbation.
- Perverted thoughts about sex e.g. incest, rape etc.
- Using sex as a way of asserting power.
- Having sex outside of meaningful relationship.
- Being unhappy with your sexuality.
- Being a slave to your sexuality. Your sexuality controls you – you don't control your sexuality.
- Getting involved in sexual activities which go against your own principles.
- Drained energy or disrupted sleep, due to sexual activity.

We will discuss some of these ideas in more detail. But firstly we need to consider whether sexual problems are a *cause* or *symptom* of depression:

1. **Cause:** Sexual problems <u>can</u> contribute to depression.
2. **Symptom:** Depression <u>can</u> lead to sexual problems i.e. the problems are a symptom or coping mechanism.

Sexual problems can be an underlying cause of depression (though seldom exclusively). At other times sexual problems can be a coping mechanism or symptom of depression.

Sexual problems <u>can</u> be an underlying cause
Sometimes depression can come from sexual issues. Let's look at an obvious example. If the issue is "disrupted sleep due to sexual activity", this is going to contribute to depression. We have already discussed how sleep affects depression (p.61). In fact, most of the sexual issues listed on the previous page <u>could</u> <u>contribute</u> to depression. I will deal with some of them in more depth later.

Sexual problems <u>can</u> be a symptom
When we feel low there is a tendency to want to find some way of filling that empty chasm. Some people run to the fridge, some eat a whole chocolate bar, and others turn to alcohol. People also turn to pornography, sexual fantasising, or sex as a way to fill the gap or void in their life. But what is the gap they are trying to fill?

Sexual problems often stem from feeling powerless. It's extreme, but the most obvious example of this is in the instance of rape. Why does rape happen? Why would a person get gratification out of such a vile act? Most likely the perpetrator feels powerless in life – and rape gives them some sense of power over the victim. But it's not just rape. Feeling powerless is often a root cause of sexual issues. People turn to pornography, masturbation, constantly fantasizing about sex, or sleeping around in attempt to feel powerful.

When people are depressed they often feel powerless. As a result, depression can lead to sexual issues. But we must remember that these issues, in themselves, are not the main problem, they are simply coping mechanisms. Often the deeper roots of the sexual issues are feeling powerless or unloved.

**Sexual problems often stem from
feeling powerless, unloved and unwanted.**

The problem is that our sense of power and acceptance shouldn't derive from sex. Power comes from character and knowing your true identity, value, worth and meaning. In fact, if you can control your sexual thought life – it shows you have great strength.

**Power comes from character. To control your
sexuality shows great strength of character.**

Remember the image of the ping-pong balls on page 43. We don't get rid of depression by trying to dig it out, we instil the opposite. Rather than trying to focus on dealing with sexual issues, I suggest it is better to focus on developing healthy relationships, your character and self-esteem.

Don't focus on the problem. Focus on the antidote.

Sexual problems <u>can</u> create a spiral effect

Because sexual issues can be both a contributing cause or a symptom, sexual issues can often create a spiral effect. For example, consider the following:

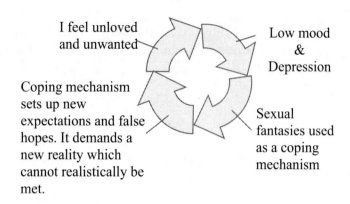

I feel unloved and unwanted

Low mood & Depression

Coping mechanism sets up new expectations and false hopes. It demands a new reality which cannot realistically be met.

Sexual fantasies used as a coping mechanism

Pornography

Pornography for many is likely to be a coping mechanism; however it creates false hope. Pornography is an unrealistic portrayal of reality. By looking at pornography it sets unrealistic expectations. Someone may create false expectations of who they want for a partner, or how they want their partner to perform, then feel low when they can't fulfil those expectations.

Pornography can take over people's lives; it can waste time and money, and lead to health issues. Furthermore pornography is degrading of women (not exclusively). If mentally someone is practising degrading thoughts, these are likely to spill over into real life – resulting in treating the opposite sex as objects rather than human beings. Pornography is an addiction. You may need to seek further help in order to stop.

Human being are not objects.
Pornography sets up false expectations.

Pornography doesn't make you
powerful. It drains you of
power and energy.

The Pill

The pill is notorious for inducing depression.[44] Why are you taking the pill if it is going to make you depressed? Think about it logically: would I rather have sex and be depressed, or abstain and feel more mentally well. Perhaps there is pressure from your partner. If your partner loves you, he will be more interested in your mental health than being with you for sexual reasons. In order to deal with this you may need to pluck up courage and speak to your partner. You should not feel coerced into taking the pill, nor should you feel guilty for refusing to take it.

Premenstrual Depression

It is useful for men to know that women's mental health may be affected by their monthly cycle. It is important to remember that her feelings and emotions will pass; that she will feel normal again. It might be that as a partner you need to treat her with a bit more compassion.

Sexual identity

For some reason we pigeon-hole people according to their sexual orientation, race, and colour. In society we hear the words "Heterosexual", "Homosexual", "Bisexual" etc. Why should someone be identified by their sexual preference? How often do we identify people by the type of drink they have? We don't say "Here come the coffee drinkers" and "Here come the tea drinkers." Why should sexuality define us any more than our other attributes?

Your sexuality is an attribute, it doesn't define your identity.

When we root our identity in our sexual thoughts, successes or failures we are heading for danger. Our lives are more than our sexuality.

Peer Pressure

Peer pressure is a large aspect of sexual health. There may be a tendency to feel that you are missing out if you are not living the life that everyone else "seems" to be leading. The media portray the idea that everyone is living a rampant sexual life. Films and TV programs portray an unrealistic view of reality. How many STDs has James Bond got? How many accidental pregnancies have happened during James Bond films? How many women's hearts have been ripped out? In films we may see the action and sensuality but without seeing the aftermath or effects. This can lead people to have unrealistic expectations.

Don't let society define your sexuality.

It is strange to think how society has changed. One hundred years ago it was frowned on to have sex outside of marriage and a lot of people may have only had one partner for life. Now peer pressure seems to suggest the opposite, that if you haven't had sex before marriage there is something wrong with you, and the more partners you can sleep with the better. If you compare yourself to the views of the media you may think you are missing out, but the media portray an unrealistic view of sex.

The media portray an unrealistic view of sex.

If you start asking your friends about how their sex lives compare to the current media view, you will most likely find out that you are probably not so different and that the portrayal of sex in the media is completely unrealistic.

Peer pressure is a strong force.
But the one who controls
his own life is powerful.

Sexual Freedom versus Slavery

"Physical freedom" is different to "Mental freedom". Consider the following definitions of a slave:

> Slave: "A person who is excessively dependent upon or controlled by something."[45]

> Slave: "A person whose life is dominated by a specific activity or thing"[46]

We like to think that we are in control of our lives. However, at times we can become so excessively dependant upon certain activities or things that we actually become a slave to the things we initially wanted to control. Has the slave trade ended? I don't think so. Our hearts and lives are still slaves to things and activities. People are slaves to cigarettes, work, money, sex, lust, power, words, food, TV, mediocrity, apathy etc. The following quotes sums up slavery:

> **"I didn't know I was a slave until I found out I couldn't do the things I wanted"**
> *Frederick Douglass*

None of us want to be slaves. Being a slave will make us depressed and steal hope. We all want freedom. But do we have the correct concept of freedom? We often think of freedom as being "physical freedom to choose anything we want". But physical freedom is different to "freedom of the heart (mental freedom)"; in fact at times they can work against each other.

Suppose Jeremy lived next to an "Eat as much as you like" restaurant and the owners said he could come and eat there for free, as often as he liked. The restaurant has 100 different main dishes and 100 different desserts. That is physical freedom to eat any food and at any time. His appetite is not restricted by money and choice. But after a year of eating there every day, how do you think Jeremy's life would turn out? Would he be a slave to food? Would his stomach control him? If he tried to stop – could he?

Suppose we fast forward 10 years. Jeremy is now considerably overweight and finds it difficult to climb the stairs. Frederick Douglas's quote sheds light on this topic. Jeremy didn't know he was a slave until he found out he couldn't do the things he wanted; he couldn't climb the stairs to his apartment.

Physical freedom: Jeremy can eat whatever he chooses.

Mental freedom: Little. Jeremy's appetite controls him. He has become a slave to food.

Compare this to Olivia. Olivia lived next to a restaurant. The owners said she can eat there for £3 at a time, only once a day. The menu only has 10 different dishes and the portions are a healthy size. It may seem like she has less freedom to eat. However, fast track 10 years and she is sprinting up those stairs.

Physical freedom: Olivia has less physical freedom in terms of what she can eat.

Mental freedom: Olivia's appetite doesn't control her. She has mental freedom.

The idea of "physical freedom" versus "mental freedom" can also be applied to the topic of strong sexual desires. People can think that pornography, sleeping around, and sexual fantasies can bring them happiness. They see it as freedom. However, just like Jeremy's restaurant "physical freedom" to do those activities, can actually make their hearts a slave to those things.

Consider Leo. Leo thinks he has freedom. He is very rich and decides to go to a strip club. He gets given a brochure of girls to choose from. He can watch any girl. He may have "physical freedom" to choose from a range of girls, but what is becoming of his heart? 10 years pass. Do you think Leo will be able to control his sexual desire? Will he have become a slave to his sexual desires? Do you think his appetite for sex will control him? Besides, what has become of his sexual appetite? Consider the following:

"Now suppose you came to a country where you could fill a theatre by simply bringing a covered plate on to the stage and then slowly lifting the cover so as to let every one see, just before the lights went out, that it contained a mutton chop or a bit of bacon, would you not think that in that country something had gone wrong with the appetite for food?"[47]

Fast forward another 10 years. Leo wants to start a deep intimate relationship with a girl and get married. Leo finds it difficult to maintain his relationship. He still goes to striptease once a week. Leo didn't know he was a slave until he found out he couldn't do the things he wanted; he couldn't seem to love his wife and dedicate himself to her. He was constantly distracted by other women. Leo did not live in a physical prison but he had become a prisoner of himself.

> **Physical freedom:** Leo can choose any girl he wants to in the strip club.
>
> **Mental freedom:** Little. Leo is a slave to his sexual appetite. It interferes with forming a meaningful relationship.

Another example of becoming a slave to sexual desires is demonstrated through the story of Henry. Henry was a student and addicted to pornography. He was in the habit of comparing girls on the Internet and sexually fantasising about them. Henry went on a beach holiday with his girlfriend. On the beach there were plenty of other beautiful girls. He wanted to enjoy his girlfriend's company and relax with a book. However, Henry was frustrated that he couldn't seem to focus on anything else than the other girls. He didn't know he was a slave to his sexual desires until he found out he couldn't do the things he wanted; his sexual thoughts controlled him. Henry was a slave to pornography. On arriving home he needed to study but kept on getting distracted by the Internet. He couldn't seem to stop the force within himself driving him to it. He thought it was freedom to look at pornography. Instead the pornography controlled him.

Now suppose you came to a country where you could make money by filming an actor put a covered plate on a table. He slowly reveals a lamb chop and then eats it. Men and women sit on their couches or at their computers drooling over the lamb chop. Sometimes they even pay to watch these videos. Would you not think that in that country something had gone wrong with the appetite for food?

> **Physical freedom:** Henry thinks he has freedom to look at any girl on the Internet.
>
> **Mental freedom:** Little. Henry is a slave to pornography. He cannot study, dedicate his thoughts to his girlfriend, and manage his time.

A further example is of Vladimir. Vladimir is a billionaire. He can afford to sleep and hire women at will. He is constantly talking about women and their sexual physicality. He whistles at women and talks about them in a derogatory way. He thinks he has freedom. And sure he has "physical freedom" to be with many women. However, mentally his heart is empty, his physical freedom to "use" and "hire" women has not brought him happiness. He doesn't realise that his heart is locked up in a prison. He has little freedom in his heart; he is a mental slave.

Now suppose you came to a rich billionaires house. He had a fridge with 100 different types of lamb chops. He was obsessed with talking about lamb chops. On his yacht he would talk about his lamb chop collection and comment on the different attributes. When entering a supermarket he would stare at the lamb chops, whistle at them and say "I could do with that lamb chop being in my collection". Would you not think that something had gone wrong with the billionaire's appetite for food?

Physical freedom: Vladimir has freedom to sleep with any girl.

Mental freedom: Little. Vladimir has no mental freedom. He has no sense of identity because he has no meaningful relationships.

"Physical Freedom" doesn't always equate to "Mental Freedom"

People can become slaves to their sexual desires.

Why would you want to be a slave to anything?

Again you may ask, what has all this to do with depression? Some people believe that all sexual thoughts are normal. I hope you can see from the examples above that it is possible to have unhealthy sexual desires and appetites that will only lead to misery and frustration. Statistics show that people who struggle with relationships, who sleep around, and look at pornography are more likely to suffer with depression.[48] Being a slave to anything is going to steal hope.

319

What is it that we are really searching for in sex?
Because sexual issues are related to depression it is important
to consider what we are really searching for in sex.

I think deep down what we are all looking for is love,
relationship and identity. Unfortunately, we have been fed
various ideas in western culture that do not always help. When
we greet a stranger we ask: "What do you do?" "What are
your qualifications?". We've been led to believe that identity is
defined by work and qualifications. In contrast, in tribal
communities a stranger may ask: "Who do you work for?"
"Which tribe do you belong to?". Both those questions are
centred around relationship. Should we get our sense of
identity from relationships, rather than work or education? Or
should it be something else?

Where do you get your sense of identity from?

Unfortunately, some people believe that "sex" _is_ relationship.
That is not true. Food is not lamb chop. Lamb chop is a type
of food. Sex is a part of a relationship. Sex is a meaningful
expression between two people who love each other. Sex
should grow out of love. If sexual feeling is rooted in
selfishness and greed then that is lust, not love. Lust is
unhealthy and leads to promiscuity. Statistics show that people
who have a promiscuous nature are more likely to suffer from
depression.[49] Sleeping around with different partners leads to a
lot of shallow meaningless relationships. Just like Leo and
Vladimir, those people find it much harder to develop and
maintain meaningful relationships. We need meaningful
relationships. Meaningful relationships bring us hope.

How to deal with strong sexual desires?
Because sexual issues are a factor in depression, it is important
to deal with them appropriately. Feelings can get us into
trouble if we follow them. If you just followed your feelings

every time you craved a chocolate bar, you could find yourself with an addiction to chocolate and could become a slave to it. At times we have to distract our thoughts and feelings, and resist temptation. Perhaps you've never tried to resist sexual temptation.

"No man knows how bad he is till he has tried very hard to be good. A silly idea is current that good people do not know what temptation means. This is an obvious lie. Only those who try to resist temptation know how strong it is. After all, you find out the strength of the German army by fighting against it, not by giving in. You find out the strength of a wind by trying to walk against it, not by lying down. A man who gives in to temptation after five minutes simply does not know what it would have been like an hour later. That is why bad people, in one sense, know very little about badness – they have lived a sheltered life by always giving in. We never find out the strength of the evil impulse inside us until we try to fight it."[50]

I like the concept of time C.S. Lewis suggests here. We sometimes think that desires are so strong we simply have to give into them. What if that temptation lasted 10 minutes and you gave up after 9 minutes and 58 seconds?

One day a wife became furious with her husband and was tempted to kill him. She'd been told by her best friend that her husband had cheated on her. She'd even been given a photograph of her husband with the other woman. The wife took a gun out of her handbag and pointed it at her husband. The desire to kill him was strong. 19 minutes went by. The husband kept telling the wife that it wasn't him, that there must have been some mistake. At 19 minutes 59 seconds she shot her husband. At 20 minutes the phone rang. The police informed her that the photograph had been faked. She'd killed her innocent husband. If only she'd waited one second. "Oh but the temptation was so strong," she exclaimed to the judge.

So often we hear people say "I just couldn't help myself." How do they know? Perhaps one second would have made all the difference between a saved marriage or ruined one. Perhaps a 5 minute jog around the block would have made the difference. "Oh but wouldn't it be better just to get it out of my system!" you may cry.

Lucy loves chocolate. She opens a chocolate shop. She is really tempted to eat the chocolate. "I just need to get it out of my system," she says. "I can't repress and suppress my feelings any longer". So she eats all the chocolate in the shop. The next days she restocks. She says two days later: "I just need to get it out of my system". Can you see how ridiculous this is? She is not getting it out of her system at all. In fact, she is feeding her desire for chocolate.

In the short term strong desires may seem uncontrollable, but we need to learn to control and abstain from feeding any unhealthy desires. In that way, they will reduce over time. What would happen if you fed a weak stray cat, would it go away? No it would come back; the more you fed it the stronger it would become and the more often it would visit you.

Strong unhealthy sexual desires are similar to stray cats. If they are fed with pornography, dirty jokes, or acted upon, they will become stronger; leading to more sexual frustration and mental slavery.

Sadly, some people think that if they form a relationship sexual cravings will totally subside – this is not true. Married couples still have times when they feel sexually frustrated or have lustful thoughts. Having a partner does not guarantee that sexual problems will disappear.

So how do we avoid feeding unhealthy sexual desire? If you have strong sexual feelings, one of the best ways to deal with them is to _distract_ yourself until the feelings subside. I specifically use the term *distract* here rather than *resist*. Remember the analogy of the ping-pong balls and water. We don't focus on getting rid of depression, we focus on pouring in hope. Likewise, you shouldn't focus on getting rid of unhealthy sexual desires but focus on building healthy desires and healthy relationships.

We have to make small choices, refuse to act on any lustful compulsions and focus our minds elsewhere. As we do so any unhealthy sexual desire will begin to subside; just like a stray cat would get the message if we refused to feed it. Learning to channel unhealthy sexual thoughts can be a good way. Exercise, music and other adrenaline based activities can help deal with these kinds of thoughts.

Unhealthy sexual thoughts are like stray cats, the more you feed them, the stronger and more frequently they will visit.

Another way lust can be reduced is to build self-esteem. Often we can misinterpret feelings as being sexual. Sexual thoughts can be a by-product of feeling extremely insecure, insignificant, and unaccepted. People think that if they give in to pornography, one-night stands, affairs etc., they will feel more loved. Focusing on building strong friendships, marriages, and instilling hope, significance, acceptance and security can relieve those unhealthy sexual desires.

Remember, once you are moving forward, don't think about the past. If you think about the land from which you have just come from, you'll give yourself an opportunity to return to it. Focus on where you're heading. Remember the analogy of the fireman on page 249. Focus is key. Do you think a fireman running into a building to rescue a baby, will be worrying about his sexual issues? No. So get focused and any depression stemming from sexual issues will begin to subside.

Summary

- Tastes can become familiar. We need time to find out what we truly like in life, to be open-minded, and to try.

- Loneliness drains our hope and energy levels. Humans need each other. You may think socialising is tiring – but rumination on your own requires more energy than socialising. Socialise despite your feelings. If you wait until you feel ready, you'll never start.

- Family issues can be difficult to resolve. Be aware that parents can put too much hope in their children – this is unhealthy.

- Work is a large part of our life. Don't hide away if you have issues, talk about them openly with your boss. Also, make sure you are taking sufficient breaks.

- Money and fame don't bring happiness. A lot of people put their hope in gaining these but they seldom satisfy – just think of Robin Williams. Besides, being rich or famous has a lot of drawbacks. With great privilege comes great responsibility.

- Sexual problems will steal hope. They often stem from feeling powerless. Our sense of power shouldn't derive from sex.

- When we root our identity in our sexual thoughts, successes or failures we are heading for danger. Our lives are more than our sexuality. Don't become a slave to your sexual thoughts. It is when you control your sexuality you have great power.

Finding Hope During Illness

At some point in life a lot of us will face an illness that is likely to erode hope. Long-term illnesses such as diabetes, chronic fatigue, migraines, backache, or arthritis can drive us to despair. Whilst I have never suffered a terminal illness, such as cancer, I hope I can offer some advice.

As a child I frequently had migraines. Normally rest, a migraine tablet, a cup of tea, and lying down in a darkened room with a flannel over my eyes would relieve the problem. I would usually fully recover by the next day. Whilst I can't say for certain what caused the migraines, I do believe they were mainly triggered by bright lights. Flash photography and fluorescent strip lights seemed to be culprits. Often, if I ran from inside to outside on a bright summer's day, a migraine would start. After becoming aware that bright lights seemed to trigger migraines I avoided bright lights. As a result, the frequency of migraines seemed to reduce.

I hadn't had a migraine for years. On the 24th of May 2018 one started. Unusually this strong migraine continued for 4 consecutive days. A week later, even though the intensity had dropped a little, I still felt as though I'd been hit over the head with a rounders bat, that someone was holding stinging nettles on top of my head, that I'd just come off an extreme ride at a theme park, or had been on a rough sea voyage. I felt nauseous, slightly sick, had blurred vision, earache, neck-ache, and a headache. In the initial stages the headache was so severe that I was only getting three hours sleep a night; it then reduced to about 40% of the intensity. Ten weeks have passed and I still feel ill. I still feel as though someone has tightened a clamp around my head and screwed it tight. During these 70 days of chronic headache I have been up and down emotionally; at times been driven to the depths of despair. I have also monitored my feelings and noticed what has given and stolen hope.

Fear of the unknown

The first weeks were the most hellish – simply from not knowing what was going on. Having an unknown diagnosis is difficult. Initially the doctor thought it was a migraine stuck in my system so gave me some extra strong medication. She advised that if it failed to work I should go to the Accident and Emergency department. It failed to work, so I headed off to A&E. I was paranoid about what was going on. A&E decided that I had a strong migraine and tried to flush my system with an even stronger drug – but that failed to work, and they dismissed me, informing me that I didn't have a migraine. This left me in a state of worry. If it isn't a migraine what could it be? I went for an eye examination. The opticians said that they could see no abnormalities. I returned to my doctor who then suggested I had neuralgia and referred me to the physiotherapy department. The physiotherapy department advised that they couldn't help with this problem, as it didn't look as though I had neuralgia relating to posture or neck related issues. Subsequently, I was referred back to my doctor and then the neurological department.

Note here, that in writing this, time is condensed. Referrals don't usually happen within 24 hours – there are often weeks of waiting – and this waiting to be seen – waiting for a diagnosis – is painful and provides plenty of time to worry. "What if" questions arise and steal hope. "What if I have a brain tumour?", "What if I have brain damage?", "What if I've had a stroke?".

Thankfully I was blessed enough to get two short notice cancellations: an assessment with the neurology department, and another for an MRI scan. My MRI results were normal and the doctor diagnosed me as having chronic migraine. The initial diagnosis by the doctor was most likely correct; it's just that the drugs prescribed by the surgery and A&E failed to work. Having a diagnosis was a relief! I could feel my spirit breathe again. Having a diagnosis can bring hope because it rules out all the other possibilities and the associated fears. Am I better? No. I am writing this with a headache, and slightly blurry eyes. I have to use a special filter on the computer screen in order to type this. However, emotionally I am now much more on top of this illness because I no longer fear the worst case scenario and fearing the unknown. Having fear of the unknown on top of an illness makes everything worse.

Receiving a diagnosis is only half of the story. There are also many other things that will affect your levels of hope during illness. Firstly, other points made in this book have been useful in finding hope during illness. And interestingly, I can also in retrospect, project some lessons I have learnt during these 10 weeks back onto my understanding of general depression. The following are observations I've noticed during this period.

Don't own your illness

One of the first things I remembered during the initial weeks of this migraine was the importance of not owning the illness. On page 9 I explained this using an analogy of a hire car. It's much easier to let go of a physical pain if we don't believe we own it. This physical illness doesn't define me – it's not part of my identity. I don't _have_ a headache – it doesn't belong to me – I am just _experiencing_ one.

> **This illness is not controlling me.**
> **I am just experiencing it.**

Not owning your illness means you need to be careful how

you talk about it. Watch your words and be aware that talking about pain may psychologically increase it.

**Talking about a pain may
psychologically increase it.**

Reaching out

When we find ourselves in a dark place we can either close up or reach out. Both have dangers. On the whole reaching out is better, but we have to be careful who we reach out to and guard ourselves from potential pitfalls.

During the initial weeks I was keen to tell people what I was suffering with. If someone asked "How are you?", I had a tendency to tell them the truth. The first reason for this is I want to be honest. The second reason for telling the truth is that I was also hoping those people would offer hope – that somehow they might have an answer. However, I soon came to realise that reaching out is not always beneficial. Consider the following people who reach out.

Leila

Leila has an undiagnosed illness. She is struggling with undiagnosed headaches. Whenever she meets her friends, the hairdresser, shopkeepers etc. she tells them her issue. Her best friend says "Ah yes. That is occipital neuralgia. I had that – and with some neck exercises it went after a few weeks". Her hairdresser tells her "Ah yes. That is occipital neuralgia. I had that, and with some neck exercises it went after a few weeks".

In this instance Leila's contacts have given her hope. She seems to have found a solution. She believes this will pass.

Sean

Sean is also suffering from extreme headaches and similarly reaches out to those around him. The barber tells him "Oh yes. I had something similar. It's occipital neuralgia – just do some neck exercises." His best friend tells him "Oh yes. I had exactly the same type of headache – you must be allergic to gluten. I cut out gluten and the headache went." A shopkeeper tells Sean that his headaches must be from sleeping in the wrong position.

Each of these elements may offer hope in themselves. However, after reaching out to so many people Sean may now be left confused: "Could it be this?", "Could it be that?". His thoughts spin in circles. The confusion adds to his stress. And this kind of confusion is becoming more and more common. Due to the recent explosion of advice on the internet everyone thinks they have some knowledge. If you share your illness, suddenly everyone else wants to try to diagnose what you have and become your doctor – this can lead to confusion. And confusion steals hope.

Pete

Pete is also suffering with headaches. He tells his friends the symptoms. His friends come back with a variety of answers: "Wow that sounds serious. You could have a brain tumour." "You need to get your head scanned immediately." "My uncle had undiagnosed headaches just before he died." "It's occipital neuralgia – my husband committed suicide after he got that."

Poor Pete. In trying to reach out for help he reaped negative and fearful reactions. If these headaches were serious, wouldn't the doctor have sent him for an immediate scan? Are these reactions just tearing down the trust of the medical profession; saying doctors don't know what they are doing? The reactions of Pete's friends could send Pete into a spiral of negativity and despair. Those friends trying to play doctor have unknowingly fed Pete's fears.

Amy

Amy has an undiagnosed illness. She reaches out to a colleague at work. The colleague tells her that she also suffered similar symptoms and that it was a chronic migraine. She told Amy that an osteopath could help relieve the symptoms. Amy followed the advice and it worked.

In reality, each of these characters suffered from chronic migraine. The first three (Leila, Sean and Pete) did not have occipital neuralgia. By reaching out, each of these characters were offered advice and this affected their levels of hope as follows:

Leila: false hope – it wasn't occipital neuralgia.

Sean: despair from confusion.

Pete: despair and fears that something worse may have happened.

Amy: true hope.

Whilst these are distinct examples, in reality you will often find a mixture of responses. I met a lady in the park and she asked me how I was. In my honesty I shared that I was struggling with chronic headache and blurry eyes. She said she suffered with the same problem many years ago. At that point my hope level rose. She said that due to a treatment all her headaches had gone. Great! My hope went up another notch. But then she told me her eyes had never recovered and she still had blurred vision. My heart sank. She had just sown two pieces of hope for healing, then by telling me about how her eyes never recovered, sown a seed of despair.

At this point I realised I had a choice. I didn't have to let her experience determine mine. I could hold onto the hopeful words and tell myself: "This problem is curable. It can go away" and forget what she said about her eyes OR I could focus on the idea that her eyes never got better. As I went about the day the voice of "Your eyes will never get better" seemed to get louder and louder – it seemed to outgrow the seed of hope that the headaches were curable. It was torment! I couldn't simply wish this negative nagging voice away. If I focused on trying to get rid of it, it would just reinforce itself. In order to get rid of the nagging thought I would have to use replacement strategies as mentioned on page 43.

When we reach out our heart becomes like a small patch of fertile ground. Positive hopes are like plant seeds that germinate under the right conditions. In contrast, false hopes, confusion, fear and despair are like weed seeds. These despairing weeds can sometimes seem to grow quicker and outgrow the plants of hope. This is of course what seemed to happen with the news the lady in the park gave me.

If we do find ourselves in a situation where negative seeds are sown, we need to root them out, just like we dig up weeds in the garden. In order to do this I suggest replacing any worries with hopeful thoughts.

To conclude. In my attempt to find a diagnosis, and help for my unknown illness, I reached out to many people. Some people gave me hope, whilst others sowed seeds of despair – yes someone was concerned that I might have had a brain tumour. Others sowed false hope and confusion, and yet others sowed multiple seeds. Given this we need to be careful who we reach out to.

Self-Pity

One huge danger in reaching out is that we end up talking about our problem all the time. If we are constantly listening to our own problem, it will make it harder to take our mind off the pain. Also, if you are anything like me, talking about your problem can lead you into a place of self-pity. As I was passing an advertisement on a billboard I had this humorous idea of advertising my headaches on the billboard.

Self-pity won't cure your illness any quicker. It may draw the attention of others, but not the right kind of attention; it won't solicit help – it may actually turn people away. Do you know anyone who has a lot of self-pity? It's actually an unattractive quality.

When experiencing self-pity we may look at all the possible bad things we have done and look for reasons why we are ill:

- "Could I have migraines because I took that job?"
- "Could it have been something I ate?"
- "I shouldn't have been stressed about that situation."
- "I shouldn't have gone to bed so late."

332

The problem is we may never know why, where, or how we got ill. Trying to find out is not necessarily going to help. It may be a waste of energy that could be used otherwise. We have to accept that the past is the past and move on. If I continue to drive a car looking in the rear mirror, I am likely to crash again.

In combating self-pity be careful that you don't use flippant commands such as "Just get over it", "Move on", or "Let it go". They are seldom constructive. Such phrases can lead to thoughts like "I want get over it, I know I should, but I can't seem to"; you effectively beat yourself up because you can't seem to achieve the command. Beating yourself up is sometimes known as self-condemnation. It is to this that we now turn.

Self-Condemnation

As mentioned in the section on memory (see page 114), healing comes by replacement or distraction not through omission. Rather than beating yourself up, what good things can you focus on? If you see yourself doing everything wrong, the chances are you are less likely to see when you are doing things right. Besides, even if you have made mistakes, it doesn't mean that life cannot still be beautiful and meaningful.

Jessica had a beautiful glass vase worth £1000. She dropped it. Oops! Jessica had a beautiful ceramic bowl worth £1500. She dropped it. Oops! Jessica had a beautiful mirror worth £2000. She dropped it. Oops! Jessica was upset because she thought she had made a lot of mistakes. But Jessica's father was an artist. He helped Jessica. Together they took all the pieces and made it into a beautiful sculpture of a peacock. That sculpture now sits in a local art gallery and is viewed and loved by all. It's been valued at £500k.

We will make mistakes in life – that's inevitable – but mistakes can be turned into beautiful things if we pick up the pieces and look for the beauty.

We don't need to fear making mistakes, we can learn from them. Besides, without freedom to make mistakes there would be no scope for creativity. Beethoven was once composing a piece of music. Whilst playing his composition his left hand jumped down the piano keyboard and accidentally hit a wrong note. "Oh, I like that better than the note I intended," he thought. And, as a result, it stayed in the composition. Composers, painters, chefs, artists and many other people find that mistakes can bring great joy to them. Mistakes add to creativity. When we make mistakes we should be grateful we have the freedom to make mistakes.

Just like the sculpture, any mistakes you make in life do not make you less valuable or less beautiful. What's more, despite making mistakes, YOU are no mistake. I repeat YOU are no mistake. You are very valuable and a beautiful act of creation as your parents conceived and gave birth to you. You are intended to be here. You are significant, loved and accepted.

Lies and Doubts

Firstly, let's distinguish the difference between "Doubt" and "Questioning". These words are often used interchangeably, but there is a difference. Doubt is defined as:

> "to incline to believe only with uncertainty and
> fear; to distrust; a suspicion"[51].

Doubt is different from questioning in that it is of negative bias; it starts with a pessimistic outlook. Questioning starts from a level playing field or neutral standpoint. Consider the following:

A company is interviewing candidates for a new job as a product designer. When the interviewer enters the room their intent should be to "question" the candidates. They start from a neutral standpoint – with a blank slate. As they ask questions, it leads them to conclusions – such as "This candidate is wearing scruffy clothes", "this candidate is really good at articulating himself" etc. This then leads to a positive or negative conclusion.

In contrast, if an interviewer started her day in a bad mood, she might come to the office and say: "None of my candidates are going to be good. We had rubbish ones yesterday – so all of them are probably going to be bad today". That is doubt. Her attitude towards the candidates has a negative bias. That negative bias is not grounded in the reality of the situation.

As we can see above, there is a difference between doubting and questioning. And this will be evident in how we think and act. "Doubt" is planning or acting as though it will or won't happen, actively holding and rehearsing the negative. "Questioning" is simply not being sure, parking the issue, and then proactively waiting for an answer to come.

Returning to illness. When you are suffering with an illness, lies and doubts will come. Firstly, we need to recognise them. Doubts will often include words like "Never" e.g. "I shall never get better". "What if" statements are also common e.g. "What if my eyesight never recovers?"

Secondly, as we recognise our doubts, we need to doubt our doubts, and bat them away. We don't have to let them settle. Don't let them take root like weeds. Uproot them as soon as possible. But note, this is not simply an act of will power though. Doubt isn't simply wished away. It needs to be challenged with the truth. During this period someone once said to me "Stephen, you need to believe you will get better".

This is not helpful. I know I need to believe and that doubts are plaguing me. Saying such phrases only makes one feel shameful and guilty for not believing – it doesn't help the person believe. It's like saying "You need to stop smoking cigarettes" to a smoker who wants to give up. They will reply in their head "Yes – I know the problem – this is exactly what I am struggling with – now I feel even more guilty inside. This is something I should be able to do and I can't seem to, therefore I'm a failure." So if you are trying to help someone please do not say things like "You need to believe you will get better" it's not helpful. Besides, this assumes that you can just believe anything into existence. Try saying it to someone who is dying "You need to believe you will live to 400 years old". In order to rid of doubt we need the truth. Not just vague truth, but specific truth. Don't say to yourself "don't doubt" - that's unhelpful. Replace doubt with truth and trust.

If the doubt is "What if the doctor missed something? What if I have a brain tumour?", we ideally need to have a specific negation of that doubt – such as "I don't have a brain tumour because the MRI scan was clear". If we don't have a specific answer we need to wait. If I haven't had an MRI scan, I can tell myself: "The doctor said I haven't got a brain tumour, she is experienced and therefore I must trust her judgement." While I am waiting for a result I can focus on the doubt, and wait with stress, or I can distract my thoughts and allow peace to come in.

**Thinking about a doubt won't make
the truth arrive quicker – it will
only reinforce the doubt.**

The worst thing we can do with a doubt is speak and rehearse it out loud. If you are physically speaking it out loud, you will be hearing it with your ears and this will only reinforce the doubt stronger in your memory. If you have doubts, learn to keep them silent or only talk about them to appropriate people in a constructive manner whereby you overcome that doubt. If you do catch yourself doubting – forgive yourself and then guard your thoughts and mouth. Words have power.

Some common doubts that can whir around our minds when we are ill are:

"What if I don't get better?"

"What if I never recover?"

If you catch yourself thinking these, try to replace them with the opposites:

"What if I **do** get better?"

"What if I **do** recover?"

This is not ignoring the possibility that illnesses don't always subside, but it is a much more hopeful outlook.

What if I do get better from this chronic migraine? I will celebrate! When I get better I plan to take a drive, buy a nice meal and treat myself to a holiday. What is your plan for when you get better? Be careful your plan is not time based – unless you are certain about the timing of your healing. If you are unable to fly due to sickness, you shouldn't, for example, book a holiday in two weeks time to celebrate the recovery of your illness – because you may not be better by then. Instead you might plan to celebrate by putting some money in an envelope and saying "When I get better I will use this money to purchase a plane ticket".

Celebrate your victories

Some of us find that our lives are like pendulums of doubt. We always seem to swing back to the negative. Why?

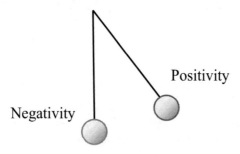

I truly believe the answer is: "Because we don't celebrate our victories enough". When did you last celebrate the remission of a headache? When did you last celebrate recovering from an illness? When did you last celebrate getting a pay cheque from work? We will easily moan at the grass not being green because it hasn't rained. But when did you last celebrate the rain falling and making the grass green? We will easily moan being stuck in a traffic jam? But when did we last celebrate travelling a journey without any hold-ups? The more we celebrate our achievements in life the more we will alter the pendulum points so that the default position is positivity.

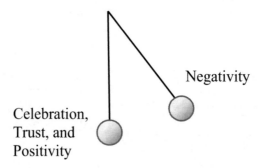

You are doing well. You should celebrate all you have achieved. You should celebrate having read this far. You should celebrate success. And most of all you should celebrate being yourself. YOU should celebrate YOU.

When we plan celebrations, if they are vague, we are less likely to carry them out. Your celebrations should be SMART celebrations: Specific, Measurable, Achievable, Realistic, and Timely. Start planning a way to celebrate recovering from your illness.

Celebrations wear away doubt
One way we can celebrate, and defeat doubt, is by recalling all the times in life when we have recovered from an illness. Be thankful for those times. In my life I've had...

Chest pains	... and recovered.
A fractured arm	... and recovered.
A pulled hamstring	... and recovered.
Multiple migraines	... and recovered.
Backache	... and recovered.
Food poisoning	... and recovered.
The flu	... and recovered.
Hay-fever	... and totally recovered.
Bent my thumb	... I haven't recovered but I can manage to the point that I completely forget I have a bent thumb.

**Let's not talk about our problems
– let's talk about our victories.**

Imagination
As we talk about our victories we will hopefully move towards the idea of recovery. I have mentioned in this book the power of imagination. I urge you to imagine recovering from your illness. It will not only calm your emotions, but it will also help with recovering or managing your illness.

The story of Air Force Colonel George Hall is quite remarkable. During the Vietnam war he spent seven years locked in a cell. That is enough to make anyone go insane. During this time he imagined he was a golf professional. He spent seven years playing golf in his mind. On release he was keen to play a round of golf. One week later he entered the Greater New Orleans Open and shot a round in 76, which is an excellent score.

"Imagination is more important than knowledge"
Albert Einstein

Knowledge

Einstein makes a sweeping statement here that imagination is more important than knowledge. This is incredible – especially given that Einstein was a very knowledgeable person. When we are ill there can be a tendency to try to figure everything out. In the western world we tend to put knowledge and reason on a pedestal and worship it. On a personal level we tend to think:

> "If I could cross every T and dot every I, if I could gain all knowledge under the sun, then I would be able to solve my own illness and find healing."

I have to admit I will never have that kind of exhaustive knowledge. I am not omniscient and any attempt to be so will just drive me crazy. I can constantly ask questions, "Why? Why? Why?", but that kind of attitude will lead to burnout. I have two options:

1. Try to figure everything out and go crazy in the process.
2. Admit I don't know it all and trust everything will turn out fine.

Knowledge alone doesn't necessarily solve problems. If I knew how to perform heart surgery, I wouldn't be able to perform it on myself. In that case relationship would be an essential addition to knowledge; I would require someone else to perform the operation. Knowledge without relationship is often useless.

Knowledge without relationship is often useless.

Sometimes we need to be comfortable with not knowing. We often think too much about our problems but reason alone won't always solve them. Yes there are reasons for most things in life. But just because there are reasons for everything, doesn't mean we should find them. Trying to find all the reasons to things in life will blow your mind and lead to confusion. Sometimes we have to stop trying to figure everything out and learn to trust.

I was once told that students of psychology or philosophy sometimes have chosen to study those subjects because they themselves have suffered from trauma in childhood. Often their studies are an attempt to find out why they suffered, to reason, justify or find solutions to their suffering. Ironically some of them don't find the answers they are looking for, and this adds to their suffering. I imagine there *may* be an element of truth to this, but clearly not all students who study these subjects do so for these reasons.

Trying to figure out why we suffer can ironically cause more suffering. Sometimes it's better to accept we've suffered and move on.

How about we get comfortable with not knowing?

Besides, why are we trying to figure everything out? Presumably to prevent further suffering.

Suffering is inevitable

If we expect to never suffer in life, we will suffer a lot of disappointment. It's not a question of whether we will suffer in life; we will. It's a question of how we respond to suffering. Being angry and bitter about suffering will not change the suffering, in fact it will make it worse. The only thing bitterness will change is your emotions. The person who hurt you, pushed you down those steps, etc. won't suffer if you are bitter towards them – you will! If they've caused you five years of pain, by continuing to be resentful towards them, they will only continue to hurt you and win the game. This also applies to yourself – don't become bitter towards your own failings. Forgive others and forgive yourself.

Let's get better not bitter.

Intrinsically suffering is bad. But instrumentally it can be useful. I am far from perfect. I would like to think that my character, skills, and knowledge of this world could all be gained through reading and reasoning – alas it can't. Sometimes we need to suffer in order to learn – especially when it needs to become heart knowledge rather than head knowledge.

If you learn how to ski by reading a book in an armchair, you will learn head knowledge and are unlikely to physically suffer. The most you might suffer is a paper cut – I've never met anyone who sprained a leg whilst reading a book. The risk of suffering is low, but by reading a book you probably won't make a good skier. In comparison, if you learn how to ski on a ski slope, you will put yourself at a higher risk of suffering a broken arm or sprained leg. But you will certainly become a better skier. Suffering shows that you are taking risks. Suffering shows that you are brave, enriching your life, and learning heart knowledge as opposed to head knowledge. Something I find particularly useful when suffering is to focus on the following saying:

> **"Suffering produces endurance, and endurance produces character, and character produces hope."**[52]

If I have the flu, I know it will pass; but I have to wait for it to pass. I don't know how long this chronic migraine will last; I am waiting. And as we wait, we can choose how we wait. I can wait in anger and bitterness, or I can focus on what I can learn during the time of suffering. I can stay in this sickness and give up, or I can go through it and get stronger. In the words of a Kelly Clarkson song: "Whatever doesn't kill you makes you stronger." The following are some questions I can ask myself while I wait for suffering to pass:

- What am I learning from this experience?
- How can I use this time of suffering to help and comfort others?
- What can I do while waiting to get better?
- How am I coping with this illness?
- My life was busy before I became ill. Can I use this time to listen to talks, read books, and do things I wouldn't have done if I wasn't ill?
- How can my character grow during this trial?

I can say with certainty that so far suffering with chronic migraine has definitely shaped my character. I am more sympathetic with people who are ill. I have spent many hours listening to motivational videos on YouTube, which I wouldn't have done if I'd been healthy. I have strengthened my character, and this additional chapter would not have existed if I wasn't going through this current suffering. Do I wish to suffer? Of course not! But whilst I suffer, I might as well try to learn something from it.

Focus Out

Of course, there are no guarantees in life especially concerning the length of time it takes to heal. How we respond in the meantime will affect our levels of happiness. If we respond by focusing in on the problem, it will most likely steal our joy. If we respond by focusing outwards, it may allow us to live a more fulfilled and enjoyable existence. If the problem lasts a long time, the human body and spirit will adapt to the illness. There are many people who in the initial stage of illness thought "I can't cope" but as time went by they adapted remarkably. I am inspired by what people achieve despite their physical illnesses. Mozart went blind and still wrote symphonies. Beethoven went deaf and continued writing music. You have much more ability to cope than you realise. You can learn to adapt over time. Adapting is easier when we focus on others and what we do have, and less on the illness. However, please note, adapting does not mean accepting an illness. You should still hope to be free one day. Still refrain from owning the illness.

When you are facing illness you are allowed to go ahead and be a blessing to someone else. In fact, as we show kindness to others it takes our mind off the pain. What's more, when we show kindness to others they are more likely to reciprocate. Acts of kindness are extremely beneficial when you are ill.

**Kindness brings hope to both
the giver and receiver.**

As we focus on other people it helps build endurance, character and hope. It also brings us joy.

"If you have a problem, it's perfectly okay for you to go ahead and enjoy your day".

Joyce Meyer

What I find remarkable about the quote above is that the person who said this, Joyce Meyer, suffered from sexual abuse by her own father for over 15 years. She calculated that her father must have raped her over 1000 times in this period. If she can find strength and hope to enjoy her life despite suffering, I believe we can too.

Value

Another thing to consider is the following:

You suffer because you are worth targeting.
You suffer because you are of great value.

Imagine knights on horses in a battle. Who does the enemy go after? The enemy wants to primarily target the prince or main commander. Why? Because it knows that if it kills the prince, then the footmen will retreat. The enemy goes after the most important knight because they are of great value and are worth targeting.

Sometimes people refer to their illnesses as "my demons". Of course, "my demons" is often a figure of speech. But let's say they existed. Why are demons unlikely to attack small stones? Simply because they aren't worth targeting; they are of little value. Why would demons attack humans? Because humans are of great value and worth targeting. The thought "I suffer because I am of great value" can give hope and peace during times of suffering.

Dealing with someone who has moments of depression

Things you shouldn't say to a person who is suffering

If you struggle to understand someone who is depressed you need to be sensitive with what you say. Will power alone can't solve depression; it's truth and instilling hope. Saying the following phrases to someone who is depressed is unhelpful:

- "Snap out it!"
- "Pull your socks up!"
- "O come on, get it to together will you!"
- "Don't be depressed – you've got a lot to be thankful for!"

Telling someone that they shouldn't be depressed is not a good idea. You may try telling them "Don't be depressed, you've got a lot to be thankful for." Whilst there is an element of truth, saying things like this can make the person feel guilty for feeling depressed and the guilt and shame can compound the depression. Depression is related to the memory and someone who suffers may find it difficult to access positive thoughts; I highly recommend reading my second book on the memory and science when it is available. Also, it is important to recognise that depression is not necessarily a permanent state. If a sufferer happens to be laughing, it is simply because he or she is having a moment's respite (see page 11).

Relativism seldom helps

If someone is depressed, relativism is not a good way to deal with the problem. For example, if someone is depressed because they are stressed in their job, you may say to them: "Well at least you have a job, and you at least have an income. Look at the people in Africa who have no jobs and no food." You may think you are helping, and whilst encouraging thankfulness is good, relativism is insensitive to the person's problem. Their problem is still worthy of attention. Take for example a scenario with a doctor:

Jill goes to the doctor with the flu. On arriving the doctor examines her and tells her she has the flu, and then says to her: "Well my last patient was just diagnosed with cancer, so why can't you just be thankful that you don't have cancer. Your problem is nothing compared to my last patient so go home."

That would be ridiculous. Doctors should take as much care and concern over a small problem or a big problem. Whilst we need to put problems in perspective, we do still need to pay attention and show sympathy to all issues.

Avoid Commands

Commands do not generally work unless the person knows _how_ to act on that command. The following example shows how futile commands are when the person has not been properly trained.

Sven is fighting in an 18th century war. He has <u>not</u> been trained how to use a cannon. The enemy is advancing with speed. Sven's officer shouts at him to get behind the cannon. The enemies' horses gallop. "Fire!" his officer exclaims. Sven has never used a cannon, he doesn't know how to operate it. Sven tries to reply "But I ...", his officer interrupts him. "Fire!" Sven panics. The horses' hooves are thundering towards them. "Fire! Fire!" the officer shouts even louder. Sven feels smaller and smaller; more and more insignificant, unaccepted, and insecure. A friend suggests practising mindfulness. It's too late. After half the army has died and he is lying in the hospital, Sven feels even more useless; he feels he has let his army down.

If Sven had known _how_ to use the cannon then the command "Fire!" would have made total sense and Sven would have felt confident and able to do that. A command needs truth and understanding before it can be used; or, at least, truth needs to be given immediately after a command. Phrases like "Stop worrying" or "Don't be anxious" can work if the person knows _how_ to achieve those things. However, if they do not know _how_ to achieve those things, such phrases can cause more frustration and feelings of failure. They can cause guilt and steal hope rather than give hope. And of course freeing yourself from depression is not as simple as firing a cannon.

348

Examples of unhelpful advice

Perhaps the best way to demonstrate poor advice is through an analogy. Let's look at a previously used analogy of Bob with his till problems.

> Bob works in a shop. He believes that 2+2=5. His boss keeps asking him to count the money in the till, but Bob keeps making a mistake. Bob has now been threatened by his boss that he will lose his job if he continues to make mistakes. Bob asks his friends for advice (listed below), but the advice doesn't help. When Bob goes back to work he miscounts the money in the till and loses his job.

Unhelpful Advice 1
"Don't worry I'm sure it will be fine"

What does this achieve? Bob may carry on worrying and this worry may also be compounded with feelings of guilt and shame for worrying. When Bob loses his job he will potentially have lost some trust in his friends, because they said it would be fine and it didn't turn out that way.

Unhelpful Advice 2
"Come on pull your socks up. You can do it"

What does this achieve? Bob may "pull his socks up"; he may pluck up courage and try to improve his performance. However, trying to act or trying to believe harder will not answer his problem. He can believe as strongly as he wants that he will keep his job, but unless he is told the truth that 2+2=4, he will lose his job. When Bob loses his job he will potentially feel even more shameful and worthless. He may think "My friends said I could do it and I didn't. This proves that I am useless. I've let my friends down too. They think I'm a failure now because they said I could do it and I didn't. It would have been easy for them. I don't fit in."

349

Unhelpful Advice 3
"Well it's only a job"

What does this achieve? A job is important to Bob. By the friends saying this, they are effectively saying: "We don't share how important your job is to you. We are not interested in your desires." Whilst objectively losing a job is not as drastic as getting cancer, we should still show love and have interest in the smallest of problems.

Unhelpful Advice 4
"Practise mindfulness"

Use with caution! What does this achieve? Bob can go to work the next morning and practice looking at the coins, at the beautiful shapes and details, but he would still lose his job. To a certain extent, it may calm his emotions and worries, both whilst he is at work and after he loses his job, but the truth would be so much more useful. In some instances saying "practise mindfulness" might be like saying "stick your head in the sand". In other instances where you have no control or responsibility in the outcome of the situation, it may be useful – for example a traffic jam.

Unhelpful Advice 5
"Don't beat yourself up so much"

What does this achieve? This may be useful if the person knows how to stop beating themselves up. However, in this situation it is unlikely to be useful. Such a command may steal hope and make Bob feel more inferior.

Unhelpful Advice 6
Quick and Easy Answers

Depression is not normally solved by quick and easy answers. Depression varies from sufferer to sufferer, so your point may not help in this instance. If you feel you can contribute, always qualify what you mean and why you think it will help.

Examples of constructive help

The following are some examples of constructive help:

Constructive Advice 1
Give the answer

Clearly if you know the underlying problem then you can tell Bob "2+2=4". However, this should be done in a way that will not make Bob feel rejected or unloved. Guided discovery or mirroring will be much more loving than confrontation. Consider the differences:

1. Confrontation: "Bob you are wrong. You believe that 2+2=5. That's wrong. It's 4."

2. Discovery: "Have you considered whether two plus two equals five?"

3. Mirroring: "I remember I once went to a shop and couldn't count my change. I accidentally gave 5 pounds to the shopkeeper because I had calculated that two plus two was five, instead of four".

Constructive Advice 2
Highlight the problem

Bob didn't even know the problem was his maths. It might be that you can detect the problem but don't know the solution. Let's say you knew 2+2 wasn't true but you didn't know the answer. You could highlight that the answer 2+2 is not five and then admit that you don't know the answer. You could then offer to help find the answer.

Constructive Advice 3
Admit you don't have the answer

If you have no idea of what the root problem is, it is better to admit you can't help, than offer some unhelpful advice, give them false hope, say a command which the person doesn't know how to achieve, or just use a current popular saying. In admitting you don't have the answer, you will show that you are not judgemental and your friendship is still important.

Constructive Advice 4
Try to relocate the person

Location is strongly linked with memory and emotion, so getting them to change location is effective. You obviously can't force someone to change their location, but you can invite them somewhere. Perhaps you could invite them to your home to watch a film, take them out for a meal, take them to a national trust garden etc. If you don't succeed on the first attempt, don't give up. The sufferer may feel as though they don't deserve your love and attention or that they are being an inconvenience. If they tend to be perfectionists or work hard, they may feel guilty for taking time out. Sometimes forceful love can be work: "No! You are coming out with us for a meal." This will depend on the closeness of the relationship.

Constructive Advice 5
Show love and hope to the person

Remember the ping-pong ball analogy on page 43. We don't try to remove depression, we replace depression by instilling hope. So this is your role. If you can think of anything that will give the other person hope, or will show them love, that is the most effective. But be aware that people suffering with depression may find it hard to receive love; so you may need to find creative ways to do so. Often the simplest of things can help. Consider the following:

- Offer to help them tidy or clean their house: Because location is closely linked with memory – a messy house will lead to messy thoughts.

- Buy them a card: If they receive a card in the post, they

can hardly refuse it. A card with some kind words can make someone's day.

- Invite them out to a meal.
- Offer to cook for someone.
- Invite them for a day out.

Constructive Advice 6
Reaffirm their identity

A lot of depression is rooted in low self-esteem. Simply reminding them of their true value can help instil hope. Remember, we are not static objects, so cannot value ourselves in a snapshot of time. You may wish to tell them the butterfly analogy (see page 142) and reinforce that they are valued, accepted, significant and secure.

When your loved one is suffering from depression

If you are parents or a partner trying to help a loved one recover from depression, you need to make sure you don't blame yourself. It is easy to go looking for reasons why your child or loved one is depressed and start thinking that you have failed them. Thoughts such as the following may plague you.

- "I haven't been a good enough father."
- "I'm an inadequate mother."
- "What did I do wrong?"
- "I've been a terrible husband."
- "If my partner had a different partner, this would have never happened."
- "It's all my fault."

STOP IT! Chances are that it is very unlikely to be you. There are thousands of depressed people who have been brought up by excellent parents. There are parents who have 5 children and 4 turn out fine and just 1 struggles with this issue. Who is to blame? Most likely not the parents. But it's simply not worth trying to figure out – blame is corrosive – it doesn't achieve anything. There are also thousands of people who have wonderful partners – so please don't feel guilty or shameful for having a loved one suffer from mental health issues. Whilst it's true that no parents or partner are perfect, the very fact that you are reading this means that you are trying to care for others.

Have patience with yourself. There are seldom quick fixes. It can be exhausting looking after your loved one with little feedback or thanks. Well done! You are doing well. And thank you for trying your best. You may not notice the rewards of your labour but I can assure you that there are rewards and without your love and support things would most likely be a lot worse.

You can't build railway tracks at right angles. Be patient.

If you are struggling to help someone who is depressed, you may feel a failure for letting them down. If this is the case, please seek help. Books, videos, the library, counsellors, doctors, a local church etc. may give you a start, or at least point you in the right direction. It is important to make sure you don't feel isolated in dealing with the problem. Don't feel ashamed to talk to friends about your struggles. Even if you are not struggling with depression yourself, it may also be useful to study depression because you might learn something that you can pass on to your loved one.

Possible influences on a loved one's mental health

Of course, we can't rule out that you *could* have done something that may have impacted your loved one's mental health. I have come across cases where parents have contributed to the poor mental health of a child – but it is unlikely. If in any way you feel something you have done may have contributed to your loved one's suffering, be brave and honest enough to discuss it. Chances are that you are over-worrying about something small. Open communication can help heal all parties. We all make assumptions in life and when left in the dark, these can fester. Often these assumptions can arise from miscommunication. For example:

As a child, Lily wanted to learn the harp. Her father told her "No! Sorry you can't!" Lily made an assumption: "My father thinks that I'd make a terrible musician", "I'm not good enough." Lily harboured bitterness towards her father for many years. Then one day she decided to open up about it to her father. "Oh, no!" her father exclaimed. "I would never have wanted you to believe you would make a poor musician. I said you couldn't, simply because we couldn't afford a harp at the time."

We often hurt those we love most, simply because there are more chances for miscommunication and assumption to take place. When we are physically sick, it is better if we vomit than keep it in. Likewise it is better to let your feelings out. If you feel that there are any areas which may cause your loved one to feel depressed, air your thoughts with them.

As channels of communication open, healing flows.

Similarly, trying to help the depression sufferer open up will help to heal issues. This must be done in an attitude of love and forgiveness – not shame and condemnation.

Shame and pain often result from the erosion of significance, acceptance and security as mention on page 245. Your loved one may have made *false assumptions* that affect these core values based on some of your parenting or partnership. Some common false assumptions are as follows:

Performance Based Assumption
False belief of loved one: My parents or partner are performance orientated. They always excel. During their studies they were frequently awarded 'A's, and financially they have earned lots of money etc. I am not good enough; my parents or partner can only love me if I perform well and meet certain expectations.

Truth: I'm sure you love your child or partner for being them. Your desire for them to perform well is simply because you want the best for them. Also, be aware that sometimes these beliefs are being passed down from one generation to the next.

Action point: Remember, what is best for you and your idea of success may not be the same as theirs. Reinforce that you love them and if you are performance orientated make sure your loved one hasn't made the false assumption of linking performance and love.

> **False belief:** My parents/partner only love me if I perform.
> **Truth:** My parents/partner want me to do well because they love me.

Passive Based Assumption
False belief of loved one: My parents or partner are always absent therefore they don't accept or value me. There must be something wrong with me.

Truth: Sadly with divorce rates at an all-time high and

increasing stress at work many partners and children believe the above lie. The truth may be that a parent is overworked and extremely exhausted by the time they come home. Consequently, they have difficulty giving quality time to their loved ones. Also, parents and partners may be deeply struggling with their own issues. A father silently suffering with chronic pain may appear passive – however, that does not mean he doesn't love his child.

Action Point: If you have been extremely busy, passive and absent make sure your loved one hasn't jumped to false conclusions about this.

> **False belief:** My parents/partner doesn't love me because they are absent.
> **Truth:** My parents/partner loves me. They struggle to show this because they are dealing with their own issues.

Remember, shame festers in the dark and blame is a waste of energy. It's corrosive achieving little. On the contrary, open channels of communication are good - they bring healing.

"If you love deeply you're going to get hurt badly. But it's still worth it." *C.S.Lewis*

"To love is to be vulnerable." *C.S.Lewis*

Remember, you are reading this and therefore you are doing well. You are a very valuable parent/partner. There is no shame. This is unlikely to be your fault. You have the potential to change your loved one's life – even if it doesn't feel like it.

FINAL WORDS

One of the key messages in this book is that depression is a memory issue. You may have found some help from reading through this book but reading in itself doesn't provide the best answer. Developing a strong and positive memory with fast reflexes is key. Therefore, don't expect this book to have solved your problems overnight. You may need to re-read passages, to write down ideas, and to meditate on the concepts of this book before you see any considerable difference to your mood. It may daunt you if you focus on too much. I would recommend you take one little section you found useful and focus on that.

We often don't see our progress because it comes in little steps. A relative or friend, who you may not have seen for a while, may see more apparent changes to your mood than you or close friends. Keep going, even if you feel you aren't making huge progress.

I highly recommend reading other books on the subject of depression, you will find these in the resources section of this book.

Keep going, there is hope!

RESOURCES

Books

These are some books I've read on the subject of depression. Whilst I don't always agree with their content you can sometimes learn more from a bad sermon than a good one, simply because you start to disagree and that in turn helps to clarify what your own viewpoints are. I supply a brief comment on the books that I've read.

General Books:
Cognitive Behavioural Therapy For Dummies,
Rhena Branch (John Wiley & Sons, Chichester, 2010)
> *'This is a wonderful book and full of real insight into how we think. I highly recommend it.'*

Boosting Self-Esteem for Dummies,
Rhena Branch and Rob Willson (John Wiley & Sons, Chichester, 2009)
> *'A lot of depression stems from low self-esteem. This is extremely useful book.'*

Overcoming Depression for Dummies,
Elaine Iljon Foreman and Laura L. Smith (John Wiley & Sons, Chichester, 2008)
> *'This is a useful book, however, I would recommend CBT and Boosting Self-Esteem as more useful.'*

Feel the fear and do it anyway,
Susan Jeffers (Vermilion, London, 2012)
> *'There is a lot of useful advice in here.'*

How to stop worrying and start living,
Dale Carnegie (Vermilion, London, 1998)
> *'Extremely good book on how to deal with your worries. Highly recommended.'*

Emotional Intelligence,
Daniel Goleman (Bloomsbury, London, 1996)
  'A fascinating read.'

Depressive Illness: The curse of the strong,
Dr Tim Cantopher (Sheldon Press, London, 2012)
  'A good read. An insightful and balanced view of depression.'

When Perfect Isn't Good Enough,
Martin M. Antony (New Harbinger Publications, Oakland, 2009)
  'The book is a really good insight into perfectionism. I highly recommend it.'

The Procrastination Equation,
Dr Steel (Pearson, Harlow, 2012)
  'The advice is really good.'

Books on the memory:
Pieces of Light: The New Science of Memory,
Charles Fernyhough (Profile Books, London, 2013)
  'This book shares some really interesting insights into how the memory works.'

A very short introduction to Memory,
Jonathan K. Foster: (OUP, Oxford, 2009)
  'This book is a really good introduction to how our memory functions.'

The Memory Illusion,
Dr Julia Shaw: (Random House, London, 2016)
  'A fascinating book about the memory.'

Not in Your Genes,
Oliver James: (OUP, Oxford, 2009)
  'Fascinating, however, his theories have a tendency to blame previous generations. Blame is not constructive.'

Books on medicine:
A Straight Talking Introduction to Psychiatric Drugs,
Joanna Moncrieff (PCCS Books; Ross-on-Wye, 2009)
   'This enlightening book reveals a lot of the problems with medicating depression.'

Manufacturing Depression,
Gary Greenberg (Bloomsbury, London, 2011)
   'This book goes into the history behind depression. It is an insightful read.'

Books on sleep and drink:
Sleep,
Richard Wilson (Self-Published, 2017)
   'A useful book on this essential topic.'

No More Sleepless Nights,
Peter Hauri & Shirley Linde (John Wiley & Sons, New York, 2001)
   'A classic book on how to sleep better.'

Kick the drink easily,
Jason Vale (Crown House Publishing, Williston, USA, 2017)
   'Alcohol is a depressive – so kick it! I like Jason's approach.'

Books with a faith aspect:
Finding Hope again,
Neil T.Anderson and Hal Baumchen (Regal Books, Ventura, USA, 1999)
   'Don't throw the baby out with the bathwater. This was written by a leading psychologist and is a very insightful and balanced book on the subject of depression.'

Get Your Hopes Up,
Joyce Meyer (Hodder & Stoughton, London, 2015)
   'A nice easy to read book, with some common sense.'

The Hope Habit,
Terry Law (Charisma House, Lake Mary, USA, 2010)
   'I didn't feel this book had much to say.'

Hope when you need it most,
Jack Hayford (Regal Books, Ventura, USA, 2014)
   'It's like you are reading a sermon. It is overtly Christian.'

The Perfectionism Book,
Will van der Hart and Rob Walle (Inter-Varsity Press, London, 2016)
   'Despite disagreeing with various parts of the book it could be useful.'

A Practical Workbook for the Depressed Christian,
John Lockley (Authentic Publishing, Milton Keynes, 2002)
   'There is a lot I disagree with, but you might learn something from its shoddy conclusions.'

Why do I feel so down when my faith should lift me up?,
Grant Mullen (Sovereign World, Kent, 1999)
   'I disagreed with a lot of the content of this book. By definition faith is a strong hope. For a lot of people, faith does lift them up.'

Switch On Your Brain,
Dr Caroline Leaf: (Baker Books, Grand rapids, Michigan, 2015)
   'There are some interesting insights here into how the brain works. I find it is probably too general to help anyone with mental health issues. They need more specific advice.'

NOTES

1 Carnegie, Dale: *How to Develop Self-Confidence and Influence People by Public Speaking* (London: Vermilion, 1998) p.17
2 The Bible: Isaiah 46:8 (New International Version)
3 Carnegie, Dale: *The Quick and Easy Way to Effective Speaking* (London: Vermilion, 1998) p.41
4 https://en.oxforddictionaries.com/definition/lifestyle
5 https://www.independent.co.uk/life-style/health-and-families/sleep-deprivation-how-affects-your-brain-tiredness-insomnia-a7809756.html
6 http://happierhuman.com/benefits-of-gratitude/
7 http://time.com/4548883/brits-not-sleeping-enough/
8 https://www.independent.co.uk/life-style/health-and-families/sleep-snooze-button-wake-morning-inertia-body-brain-experts-a8492376.html
9 http://www.empireonline.com/movies/features/list-directors-interviewed-sam-mendes/
10 Elliot, Paul: *Hitchcock and the Cinema of Sensations* (London: I.B.Tauris, 2011) p.151
11 https://www.theguardian.com/cities/2014/feb/25/city-stress-mental-health-rural-kind
12 The Bible: Proverbs 29:18 (King James Version)
13 http://www.dailymail.co.uk/news/article-2875425/Poor-live-closer-parents-rich-Distance-families-grows-person-earns.html
14 Jeffers, Susan: *Feel the fear and do it anyway* (London: Vermilion, 2012) p.59
15 http://cafeart.org.uk/
16 http://www.dictionary.com/browse/oppression
17 Jeffers, Susan: *Feel the fear and do it anyway* (London: Vermilion, 2012) p.109
18 Parker, Ol: The Best Exotic Marigold Hotel (DVD: Fox, 2011)
19 Foster, Jonathan K.: *A very short introduction to Memory* (Oxford: OUP, 2009) p.50
20 https://psychologydictionary.org/rumination/
21 Attributed to Sigmund Freud
22 https://en.oxforddictionaries.com/definition/envy
23 Anderson, Neil T: *Finding Hope Again* (Ventura California: Regal, 1999) p.66
24 Anderson, Neil T: *Finding Hope Again* (Ventura California: Regal, 1999) p.268
25 Jeffers, Susan: *Feel the fear and do it anyway* (London: Vermilion, 2012) p.141
26 https://www.collinsdictionary.com/dictionary/english/nostalgia
27 https://www.sciencealert.com/the-latest-data-suggests-you-can-only-

keep-five-close-friends

28 https://en.oxforddictionaries.com/definition/bitterness
29 https://dictionary.cambridge.org/dictionary/english/forgive
30 The Bible: Proverbs 25:21-22 (New International Version)
31 https://dictionary.cambridge.org/dictionary/english/perfectionist
32 https://en.oxforddictionaries.com/definition/perfectionist
33 https://quotefancy.com/quote/943574/Zig-Ziglar-Live-in-such-a-way-that-if-someone-should-speak-badly-of-you-no-one-would
34 https://en.oxforddictionaries.com/definition/justice
35 Jeffers, Susan: *Feel the fear and do it anyway* (London: Vermilion, 2012) p.178
36 https://en.wikipedia.org/wiki/Dunning%E2%80%93Kruger_effect
37 Carnegie, Dale: *How to Develop Self-Confidence and Influence People by Public Speaking* (London:Vermilion, 1998) p.100
38 http://www.sciencedaily.com/releases/2015/09/150909124838.htm
39 http://selfmadesuccess.com/why-do-we-procrastinate-data-behind-procrastination/
40 Jeffers, Susan: *Feel the fear and do it anyway* (London: Vermilion, 2012) p.141
41 https://en.wikipedia.org/wiki/Parkinson%27s_law
42 https://www.cnbc.com/2018/02/07/science-shows-you-can-get-more-done-by-working-less.html
43 https://www.telegraph.co.uk/health-fitness/body/heres-what-your-body-clock-actually-wants-your-day-to-look-like/
44 https://www.theguardian.com/commentisfree/2016/oct/03/pill-linked-depression-doctors-hormonal-contraceptives
45 https://en.oxforddictionaries.com/definition/slave
46 https://chambers.co.uk/search/?query=slave&title=21st
47 C.S. Lewis: *Mere Christianity* (London: Harper Collins, 2001) p.96
48 https://www.webroot.com/us/en/resources/tips-articles/internet-pornography-by-the-numbers
https://www.psychotherapynetworker.org/blog/details/677/pornography-on-the-rise-a-growing-mental-health-problem
49 https://psycnet.apa.org/record/2012-25107-001
50 C.S. Lewis: *Mere Christianity* (London: Harper Collins, 2001) p.142
51 Chambers Dictionary (Edinburgh: Chambers Harrap Publishers, 1997) p.310
52 The Bible: Romans 5:3-4 (English Standard Version)

Appendix – Choice Methods

Selection from a Limited Choice

One of the ways to ease making decisions is to limit choice. You would think that the more choice we have the better. Sometimes this is true. There are times when I filmed a lot of takes for a feature film I made. Sometimes it would be beneficial to have a lot of takes because I chose the eighth or ninth take. If I had stopped filming after the fourth take, I would not have had those better takes. However, too much choice often leads to confusion. Limiting the amount of choice can speed decision-making up and minimise the stress of making decisions.

**It's best to limit choice to minimise
the stress of decision-making.**

We can limit a set of choices in various ways. This is often achieved by eliminating what we don't want. For example, if you are choosing a bunch of photographs you could immediately limit the choice by deciding you want a landscape orientated photograph and therefore eliminate all the portrait orientated photographs.

Character based

When we select a choice, we often make them based on price, comfort, cosiness, convenience, how this can this give me more time, appearance etc. However, we hardly ever make a decision based on how it will improve or benefit our character. We touched on this before in the section on perspective (see page 147), but we include it here as a reminder.

Let's say you were trying to choose a job. You may have a particular character issue such as poor timekeeping and therefore conclude that a job as a bus driver would be the worst job in the world. On the contrary it might be the best job in the world, because it might help you develop good time keeping and build your character in that area.

Which option will benefit my character the most?

Brainstorm then Select
A lot of good diligent work is the result of narrowing down a vast choice of options. In Dale Carnegie's book on public speaking he discusses how some of the most effective speakers in the world write much more material than they need; they then go back and select all the best bits. Having a lot of choice can improve quality, but will also take you longer, and you will consequently have more decisions to make.

Selection from Advice
We weren't designed to make choices alone. If you involve others in making decisions, this will ease the process considerably. In a restaurant, a recommendation from the chef or your friends can help. Getting advice is a good way to make decisions. However, you may need to consider the options carefully.

Lots of people may have different opinions or opposing advice. If you try to please everyone you will end up pleasing nobody, you will end up chasing your tail round in circles. Also, be aware that sometimes we ask for advice to confirm an opinion we've already formed. If the advice is contrary, that can throw a spanner in the works. Only seek opinion if you are willing to have a contrary answer.

Time Imposed Selection
Self-imposed deadlines are difficult to set and maintain. Time is a good way to make choices. They normally come in the form of deadlines set by others or monetary payments.

How do we create and keep to self-imposed deadlines? In order to keep self-imposed deadlines we can invent attractive rewards. We can also use accountability to spur us on. Posting goals on Facebook such as "Going to lose 3 pounds this week" will most certainly get you going. However, be realistic – don't go overboard when setting goals. Also, realise that if you don't achieve your goals, you will most likely have achieved more than if you'd never set a goal in the first place.

Side by side Selection

If you have a limited amount of visual choices you can choose them side-by-side. For instance, you could pin seven photographs on the wall and then choose your favourite one:

Tree Selection

When there are a lot of comparisons to make, you might use a tree-based form of choosing. We can compare pairs of items, eliminating the worst until we narrow a choice down to a final one. This is sometimes referred to as a knock-out competition. It is most commonly used in sports competitions, such as the following:

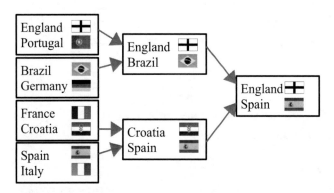

Rating Selection

If you had some criteria to rate, you could simply go through each photograph in turn and give it a score out of 10 then select the highest. This is similar to how ice skaters are chosen in an Olympic event. However, this method can be a bit misleading at times. If you start off with the worst of a series of photos but think it is good and rate it at 9, then the following ratings can be skewed by the previous ratings. There also tends to be a comparison with previous photos and this can again skew the ratings. For example, four photos are rated in two different orders:

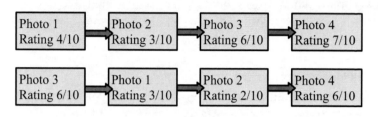

In the first instance photo 4 is rated slightly higher because it is viewed directly after another good photo so the comparison pushes its score up. In the second order, photo 4 is rated the same as photo 3 because it is judged immediately after the poorest photo which skews the following rating.

Intuition
Some people resort to intuition as a way to choose something. However, this may not always be the best way to choose something. Intuition is normally based on habit. It is possible to form bad habits and therefore you could be making foolish decisions if you rely wholly on intuition.

Toss a coin
This may be fine for deciding what to have for lunch or who should start a game of pool, but this would obviously be inadvisable for major decisions.

Pros and Cons
Listing the pros and cons of a particular options may help clarify your decision. Writing them down allows you to step back and look at the problem more easily.

Lists
Lists are useful to help us make choices. This can even be used for choosing what to do when you relax. I have a long list

of things I like to do to relax such as going to the sauna, playing snooker, or going for a walk. Sometimes when I'm tired, I find it difficult to choose what to do with my time, so instead I quickly glance down my list and sometimes it reminds me of something that I would like to do. Similarly, if you have a list of things you need to complete within the next week, it can help you to choose what to do.

Walk away and come back fresh
Sometimes undertaking research then walking away and coming back afresh can be the best way to deal with a decision. You may be more alert after a rest, and this will improve your decision-making ability.

Criteria Selection
In pubs they divide beers into various categories: Hoppy, Ruby, Stout, Porters, Dark, Light etc. By dividing things into categories, it helps us limit the choice. Can you think of any criteria you can sort your options into? For example, what is the most important for you: value for money, quality, ease of use, etc.

Criteria selection and rating can be combined together to create a "Decision Matrix Analysis". Each criterion is rated for importance, then multiplied by individual product ratings. For example, in the following table "Battery life" is rated at 7/10; fairly important. Camera 1 doesn't have a very good battery, it is rated 2/10. Multiplying the factors by individual ratings tells us that Camera 2 is the best choice. $(6\times5+6\times8+7\times7+3\times1=130)$

Criteria	Ease of use	Quality	Battery Life	Warranty Length	Rating
Importance Factor	×5	×8	×7	×1	
Camera 1	2/10	8/10	2/10	6/10	94/210
Camera 2	6/10	6/10	7/10	3/10	**130/210**
Camera 3	3/10	5/10	2/10	10/10	79/210

APPENDIX – STOP WORRYING

1. One task at a time.
2. Live just till bedtime.
3. Every day is a new life to a wise man.
4. Enjoy the stepping stones not the destination.
5. What is the worst that can happen?
6. Write your worries down: What am I worrying about? What can I do about it?
7. What are the facts? What options do I have?
8. We have to keep our emotions out of our thinking.
9. Don't procrastinate otherwise the worry will fester. Sort it out now.
10. By the law of averages what you're worrying about won't happen.
11. Circumstances alone do not make us happy or unhappy. It is the way we react.
12. Don't cross your bridges until you come to them.
13. Don't cry over spilt milk or try to saw sawdust.
14. Keep busy, but prioritise.
15. A man is what he thinks about all day long.
16. Our life is what our thoughts make it.
17. Act how you want to be, act happy even if you don't feel happy.
18. As a man thinks in his heart, so is he.
19. He who conquers his spirit is mightier than he who takes a city.
20. Exercise and eat healthily.

21. Keep a schedule.

22. A soft answer turns away wrath.

23. Don't expect gratitude from others. Give gratitude.

24. Count your blessings – not your troubles.

25. Be creative/playful, even with the dull things.

26. Be a first-rate _____ (insert your name here), not a second-rate anyone else.

27. Even if we don't succeed, what will we learn and gain?

28. Trying to please others will cause worry and fear.

29. Don't ruminate on those who are cold or you don't like.

30. We can't hope to be right more than three times out of four.

31. Rest 10 minutes during the day.

32. Think of yourself as an old crumpled sock. Then relax!

33. Talk to someone to release your worries.

34. Keep a notebook. Journal your thoughts.

35. Don't dwell on the shortcomings of others!

36. Make a schedule of tomorrow's work before you go to bed.

37. Clear your desk apart from the one issue at hand.

38. Today is the tomorrow you worried about yesterday.

39. Live today as though it were the first I had ever seen and the last I was going to see.

40. Read an absorbing book and play games.

41. What will you think of what you are going through now when you are old and you look back on it in retrospect.

42. Throw your worries in the waste-paper basket.

43. You are not going to solve all your problems lying in bed, so get up and get on with your day.

APPENDIX – COMBAT METHODS

1. Write it down and question it.
2. Assess my responsibility.
3. Don't mind read.
4. Test it out.
5. Capture and recognise the thinking errors.
6. Listen for unhelpful words. (Often superlatives and strong modal verbs e.g. "Never", "Can't", "Must", "Shouldn't have" etc.)
7. Say STOP! Don't dwell on it!
8. Be Mindful. Refocus your attention.
9. Know your triggers.
10. Schedule your time.
11. Be specific.
12. What would you say to a best friend?
13. Act as if it is already true.
14. Create counter-arguments.
15. How would you treat a child? Treat yourself the same way.
16. Exercise.
17. Eat healthily.
18. Turn your wants and needs into prefers and likes.
19. Don't label.
20. Think of someone you admire who is not a wowing success.
21. Make lists.
22. Create visual reminders.
23. Forgive and move on.
24. Remember your favourite things.

25. Admit you can't control others.
26. The journey is more important than the destination - mistakes have benefits.
27. Let thoughts drift by. Don't let them settle.
28. De-globalise.
29. Exchange negative words for positive words. Positive language affects memory.
30. Take risks – What is the worst that can happen?
31. Like personal approval, but don't rely on it as a need.
32. Tomorrow is a new day.
33. Facts before feelings.
34. I have a future.
35. Remember, I am a sum of many parts - Discard the magnifying glass.
36. Avoid alcohol.
37. Socialise despite your feelings.
38. Life would be boring if everyone was the same.
39. Don't discount the positive.
40. Give up on the "Buts".
41. Close the past.
42. Use "Therefore" to drill down to core-beliefs then challenge them.
43. Keep tabs on your progress - emotions lag – keep going.
44. Have a look at the here and now from a future perspective.
45. Do a Cost and Benefit Analysis.
46. Avoid depressing or negative music and films. Avoid Facebook for envy.
47. Help others.
48. Disappointment can be prevention.
49. Change location; your memories are linked to locations.